This Is What Doubt Looks Like

This Is What Doubt Looks Like

CAMILLE BARRIOS

PALMETTO
P U B L I S H I N G
Charleston, SC
www.PalmettoPublishing.com

This Is What Doubt Looks Like
Copyright © 2023 by Camille Barrios

First Edition

Paperback ISBN: 979-8-8229-1935-8

Dedication

To my four teammates who passed me the ball so, so many times in my youth

To my husband for being by my side through thick and thin, mostly in thin and in madness

To my girls, Isla Michelle and Mia Cassandra, for loving and cheering and for being patient with Mama

And lastly ***to myself—for believing, for trying***

My mission in life is not merely to survive, but to thrive; and to do so with some passion, some compassion, some humor, and some style.

—Maya Angelou

In third grade I received the certificate for "Most Improved 3rd Grader." I remember having mixed feelings about that. One I was happy I got to receive something to show off to my parents. I was happy to hold anything and just be recognized like my peers. Being called out meant something.

On my way home though, I remember feeling slightly embarrassed. Sad even. I let them down for not receiving a real award. Was there really anything to be proud of? Everyone else got actual recognition for real subjects and I, well, I just got a...*phrase*.

"Most Improved."

Was this made up? It felt very "by the way" to me. Like it wasn't real. Like it was a category they just threw in there because the truth was, I didn't do great in any subject. So you know here you go, hold on to this for the pictures. Ha! I felt, oh man, at the next family get-together, they'll expect me to have an award, and they'll ask me what I got, and am I really gonna brag about "Most Improved?"

Please. To be "Most Improved" meant I once failed at something, I was a freakin' failure before. So now are they making fun of me for trying and highlighting that I'm STILL not performing at top level? Oh, destroy this paper!

I mean come on?? Who the heck goes to school to be dubbed "Most Improved???" My classmates got "Best in Reading" or "Best in Math" or "Smartest in Science" and I didn't even get "Friendliest" or "Teachers' Pet?" The more I thought of it, the sadder I got.

My thinking made me so sad. Every day until probably seventh grade, I felt like I was unworthy.

Today someone could mass print that piece of paper, and I'd have it as my room wallpaper. If I could go back and just hold that little girl and tell her it means something, it is worth something.

Don't be sad. Keep going. I'm proud of you.

You are worth something.

I can't. It's done. Past is past. A moment in my history. Something to learn from.

To the younger me, thank you for not giving up. You did what you could and for that I'm happy for you. Thank you for trying. Thank you for showing up. I'll see a better version of you next year.

My self-love is self-taught.

2022 was a trying year of learning and unlearning, loving, laughing, and living. I was alone a lot but never lonely. I carried the weight, but I was never crushed.

Hey, maybe I won't get another certificate soon because I'm on a course that hasn't ended yet. That's fine. I'm not done. I'm still learning to love myself.

Signed with love,

Your "Most Improved"

You know in the boxing ring, if you get bruised and beat up but not fully knocked down, you get to rest. Recharge for a second. Then you relax, but you still feel the pain. On top of that, you must sit through the boos of the audience.

Then there's always a guy.

A guy who offers encouraging words and whispers. A guy wiping off your sweat, maybe a lil' blood from your nose. He's giving you a new mouth guard while drying your sweaty hair with a towel that's already sweaty. He says you can do it and you still have time to make the play work, but your body and mind tell you that you absolutely cannot do it anymore; in fact you don't even *want* more time.

Who is that guy? Do we know? No. Is his name on the screen? No. Will he be celebrating with you IF you even win? Ha, no. He'll clean up the mess maybe, but he doesn't get any recognition or thank you.

I don't care about that random kid, but thank gosh for him. Thank gosh for that guy.

That kid who isn't a fighter, but he's still in there with you, telling you that next time, go left instead of right. He's there giving you a massage that you barely feel because the adrenaline is too much. His voice is there to tell you that you got this even though you can barely hear.

Then time to rest is done. They push you back into the ring. The rest is a blur.

Do you win, do you lose? Does that really matter?

What mattered was that you got back into the ring when you were nearly defeated. You tried your best to knock down someone twice your size. What mattered was that even if it was painful, that kind of pain was good for you.

That pain was good for you.

It was that kid's voice of motivation, that one second of healing he gave you when you were done.

Be that guy. Be that person. That voice. Be that small strength to yourself. My six-year-old said it herself, "I am my own hero."

And when you are the one who wipes your own damn sweat, it will ALWAYS be a knockout.

"**K**eep going."

"I'm proud of you."

"I'm glad to hear you're doing better."

"I am so thankful to have you in my life."

"You are still the funniest person I know. I love being friends with you."

"Just calling because I wanted to chat with you."

"This reminded me of you, Mims."

"Of course any time, that's what family is all about."

"I'm always praying for you."

"You don't have to be sorry for anything."

"Don't be so hard on yourself. I think you're doing great."

If you have said that to me in any degree or in any way, thank you.

Thank you for filling my cup this year. For pulling me back into the light. For calling me out, and for giving me confidence. For listening without speaking, for just hearing what's in my head and heart. For being a safe place, for showing me I can be my own safe place too. For showing me that I am capable still, even if I am just a work in progress, even if I didn't hit 100% the first time, there's always tomorrow.

Thank you for your love. I wish you a blessed 2023! *Let's get it!*

Surround yourself with good energy this year and for the years to come.

If they make you laugh, if they make you smile, if they offer a shoulder, if they pick up the phone, if they break out into song with you, if they tell you that they were just thinking about you, stay there. That's where you want to be.

Life is too short to give in or stay with people who don't meet you at your level. I'm not talking looks, money, levels of education, or material things. I'm talking about energy levels.

They say that your energy is your currency, *mga anak*. I think it's true. You feel it. You'll know before the person opens their mouth. You know what I'm talking about.

It's character. Their vibration. If they make you second-guess yourself, if they make you doubt yourself, if they make you hide yourself, why waste the seconds? Why stay in that place when you can be floating to the stars?

My babies, you are so magnetic and attractive and your mind is the universe, and I think people who are there or _want_ to be in that universe with you should be there.

Only two people I know with that energy. We'll call them when you wake!

Looking at the highlights of last year, I definitely can't skip over finally coming to LA to be reunited with my friends and family.

Let me tell you why it was so important to me. Not because we were in LA. Not because of the palm trees and perfect weather and Disneyland and In-N-Out every day (c/o Isla) and finally the Shakey's I was craving for all thru my second pregnancy.

It was because I found my team again. *My team*. It stuns me to this day and makes me cry thinking that as much as I loved the Lakers ('98–'04) and idolized the Black Mamba, I never played.

Never played. I never wore a jersey, never had a coach or teammates to huddle with. I regret not trying. I regret not trying out because of my insecurities I had at that time. I thought, well, I'm short, so I'm not gonna shoot over the big guy, and I'm probably going to be picked last anyway. I thought, well, I wear glasses, so I'm probably gonna have a hard time when we get physical. Like I won't be able to dive for the ball, or I'll get pushed around too easily to make any play work.

This negative thinking, lack of self-love and confidence, and more stopped me from just...*trying*. But, Mims, if you tried and didn't make it to the starting five, well, at least you're on the bench, right? I'd still be part of it? I wish I knew that back then.

I loved playing, but I couldn't handle the outside competition and knowledge that I wasn't good enough. So I played where I was safe—with my family. And in EVERY family gathering, the ball was always passed to me.

To me!

I would be so surprised and energized every time I heard that I should have the ball in my hands. I thought, wow, really, me? Why me? I must be good! Is it true my team wants me to take the shot, even when the very serious game depended on it?

The pressure was on, one game we had in LA. Time was running down. My teammate had the opportunity to take a three, but instead she passed me the ball.

I was passed the ball.

The ball was passed to me.

Me, Mimi.

__HE-LLoOoo!!! Too much thinking, Mim!__

That second of hesitation on my end was too long—as soon as I bent my knees, I was doomed! The ball went up—wait, I don't think I even elevated! Ha!

BLOCKED. Blocked! By my cousin Henry, who so coolly shouted, "Chris Webber!"

I was so, so sad and embarrassed that I messed up the shot. The team trusted me to get that. Why, how could I? They passed me the ball, and I didn't make it. The ball didn't even see the light of day. How WEAK is that?

I was prepared to hear it. I mentally readied myself to hear that in the next play, "NEVER give it to Mimi." I was prepared to hear, "Why did you pass it? Why?" How could I miss it? It was such a simple play and I should have. Should have made it.

But you know those words never came. In fact in the next play, a plan was made. I found myself with the ball again. I did. I held my breath. I went up. The ball went up. I think it was a three, or was it a two? Does it matter? No one was keeping score! We only had TWO opponents.

SCORE!

The ball went in, and we cheered. Of course we won because of *my* game-winning shot. Inside the grown-ups asked us who won, and everyone said that we won because of *my* game-winning shot. The team said that **we won because I made the last shot**.

Tears. Just tears of joy. Then and now as I write.

Today I see this game again and analyze the play-by-play. I see it as a mom now, as a parent. When I was passed the ball, that pass was a hug, it was strength, it was courage.

I STILL don't see myself as the strongest on the team, but if I ever get a chance to pass it to someone, I will. I will.

I'll pass it to you, *anak*. That is not a guarantee that you will make it. No promise that you won't either. But whether it's a *swish* or it bounces off the rim, I will be here. To cheer you on. And I will love you. No matter what.

In sixth grade I played Oliver Twist for my school's drama club rendition of *Oliver Twist*. I remember Mr. Richardson handing out scripts to all the kids in class at the beginning of the year. I was so excited. This was what I wanted: acting, performing, being on stage, playing a character.

I was so giddy reading lines.

When auditions came I thought, please give me any part. *Please*. I mean ANY. Just anything so I could stand on stage and show my classmates what I did at home.

Mr. Richardson called out names. Everyone was assigned a character. Seconds, minutes, DAYS seemed to go by, and my name wasn't called until,

"Oliver Twist will be played by…Camille!"

It went silent for a second. Me? Did I really get a part, much less the lead? Me, who sat alone at lunch?

Some classmates broke into smiles and congratulated me for getting Oliver. I was so happy and already mapping out how I was going to tell my family, but then I heard a sharp voice say, "Camille?! Why her? **She's a GIRL!**" A couple of kids snickered. My face fell, and my smile disappeared.

I wanted to disappear.

Without skipping a beat though, Mr. Richardson said matter-of-factly, "She read better than all of you. *The part goes to Camille.*"

Silence.

I smiled through tears.

Kids softened their glares and came to hug me.

I remember practicing lines and performing on stage a lot. I loved the backstage hustle, the costumes, the directing and moving, and the "Good luck" secret handshakes.

People came to watch. Faculty, other classes. I remember emailing my teacher to watch me act as the lead. Yes, I *emailed* her, lol, because that was the time email started being a hit, and I was too shy to approach her in front of my classes.

I remember being so scared hearing the audience behind the curtain and forgetting all my lines before showtime, but as soon as I stepped into the spotlight, I delivered.

Too bad, no recording. No evidence. So this story, really, could all be made up. I have no proof of my first time being on stage. I have no proof I was there as the lead. The shows were small, elementary, and simple moments and acts, but it still meant a lot to me. It still did.

If this was made up, if I'm making this up, well, just **please let me have this story**.

When it was the last show of the semester, I remember thinking that it was OK if no one saw it. It was a good thing that no one came and recorded me because I probably wasn't that good anyway.

See that's how I felt for a long time. A very long time. I carried that with me.

If I could just go back again and hug Oliver right now, read lines with her, tell her she was brilliant.

I know I can't. Past is past. No proof, right?

This is just a story.

I was always attracted to the underdog. Cory Matthews, Peter Parker, Robin Hood, Harry Potter. They were physically smaller than the bad guys, and the world was against them all the time, but they powered through. I think a lot of narratives start this way because the audience has to identify themselves with the main character. They have to see themselves in the movie so they cheer for growth and transformation. The hero has to be flawed in some way. I mean he can't start out perfect already; otherwise, what is the movie for, right? What does he overcome?

It's hard for me not to like someone who isn't relatable. That's why in movies, I love the training montages. No sound, just the main character who is trying his or her best to improve. When they do that, the training, the practicing, to me the character looks more human, like…real.

Hercules (1997) was skinny before he trained with Phil. A demigod, yes, with super strength, but uncontrollable. Mentor needed. Steve Rogers was physically lame before he became Captain America. He trained with his troops. Adonis Creed trains with mentor

Rocky Balboa before becoming a champ. Creed has the fighting spirit because it is in his blood, but without Rocky, no direction.

I love that. I love the training part, the hurt, the discomfort, the doubt, the second-guessing. I don't like it on myself, lol, but when I watch it in movies, it's great to me, because I'm assured that the character becomes someone and, most likely, the outcome is positive. I need the training part of the story to get hooked.

I need more of those kinds of stories. I need to hear the unglamorous. The struggle. The pain. I need that for inspiration. I need it for my healing.

It triggers me when I hear "the best" or "the richest" or "the prettiest" or "the biggest house" because I don't care about that s@$!&. What's the point? Where is the beginning?

Where is the underdog? Where is the struggle? Where is the story? Where is the lesson? If there's no story, my ears are shut. If there's no fighting spirit, I'm not sold.

There's no "character build-up." If there's no struggle to overcome, I don't see any fighting spirit that emerges. If there's no fighting spirit that emerges,

I don't see a hero that is formed. If there's no hero, there's no story.

I'm going around in circles. I don't know if I got it right. Guess I gotta go back to school.

In this journey of rediscovering myself, learning self-love, and healing, I find myself looking inward. I find myself asking a very basic question: Who Am I?

Am I a fighter? A lover? Maybe both? I do a mental dance and go back in time and see myself again.

I come back to my memories, as painful or delightful as they may be, and I speak to my little self as an adult. I talk to her kindly and reassure little Mimi that things will be OK and I am loved.

Sometimes these conversations get so deep and so dark that I end up talking too loud, I forget *mi pamilya pala ako*!

Fortunately I have Isla, who calms me down and brings me back to the present. She's been so patient, loving, and understanding.

I realize though I can't ask so much of her. I, as her mom, as her example, have to learn how to control this myself. My emotional state of being, that's for ME to handle, that is MY responsibility.

NOT Isla's.

If I want her to grow up to love the world, be open to change, live life fully, then it is my sole responsibility to fix myself, heal myself, and tackle my own demons and fears. I have to have a clear head and heart for our future.

I have to do this. I'm scared; it's scary. It's painful to go back. But when I come back to reality and get to hug myself, I know I'll be OK.

Everyone knows I moved from the U.S. to the Philippines for high school, and some have asked, "How was it?" They could never get a straight answer because I always broke down in tears, lol, or I talk but never stop. My home, my family, my friends, my world, of course there was an impact. I could never answer directly, but I'll try now.

It was a grand whirlwind adventure, that's what it was. It was endearing and interesting to me how everyone was called/answered by/with their last names, more than their first. Even if they were close friends, they still called each other by their last names. I was fond of this detail so much, I remember most of my class roster in alphabetical order.

My last name was Barrios, but because I was new, I was put in the back of the girls' line.

It helped that I was next to another foreigner in line, Rena. I connected with someone. I shared my fears and anxieties as a new kid, and Rena told me it would all be fine. She told me it was OK to be a fish out of water and it was OK to be myself.

Still I was wary. I kept my guard up.

After Junior year, Rena moved back to the U.S., and I was sad about that. But I was still recovering from MY own big move, so I didn't want to be sadder than I already was. I had to try to move on.

Thankfully I met real people who liked me for me. People who didn't shoo me away for being different, people who listened when I said I wanted to tell them a story. I thank each and every one for my misadventures in high school. In the future I hope to see them again and say thank you to tell each and every one how they have touched my life. They gave me hope when I felt hopeless. When I felt so weak that I was in another world, another domain, they gave me some kind of *power*. Guess that makes me a *Power*FOOL!

I made a lot of good friends who laughed with me. We didn't speak the same language or share the same childhood jokes or know the same celebrities, but that didn't matter. It didn't matter who I was **trying** to be. No. *It mattered that I was me.* And <u>still</u> loved. And accepted. And cheered for. And they asked if they could sit next to me. Or they encouraged me to recite when I *sure as heck* did not know the answer to the Physics question. They PUSHED me to solve the Trigonometry problem on the blackboard even though I **already said** I didn't know the answer, but…for some miraculous reason…the teacher did not frown. He said it was… correct.

Ms. Fule was a teacher I admired. When I first met her, I knew she was a mom. She had that "mom" vibe, you know, caring, loving, soft but still stern voice. If I hugged her, I knew she would hug me back, but I didn't try, lol, we just met! She had shoulder-length brown hair, big, round and kind eyes, and natural rosy cheeks. I knew the teachers had to have a certain uniform, but for some reason every time I saw her, I thought what she wore was different every time. Like how many colors *are* there, exactly? Because Ms. Fule, to me, wore something different every day. But really it was the same?

Ms. Fule taught English. She helped us understand some books and essays: *The Little Prince*, *Tuesdays with Morrie*, *The Velveteen Rabbit*, to name a few. Ms. Fule also encouraged us to make a scrapbook as an assignment, a major project. I wanted to burst in tears and jump with joy! How did she KNOW that I had just recently trashed my old journals and scrapbooks and direly needed a new one? How did she KNOW this was so important to me, but I was procrastinating? **How did she know?**

So I did one. I loved what I did. I love it now. I am so very beyond happy that I have my old scrapbook from fourth year of high school. I see my old photos, my old writing, my old letters. Some candy wrappers *pa*, lol, and stickers. Thank GOSH these were not thrown away. Now I can read it with Isla. Now I can see the people who made me ME. Now I can see that what was important to me back then is just second place to my priorities now. Now I can see what was NOT mentioned back then, well, it has my whole mind and heart now. There's the growth for ya, Camille! And I have Ms. Fule to thank!

She made us do speeches in class. It was an assignment. We had to choose a good five- to ten-minute monologue from a movie, memorize it, and recite it in class. I was excited for this. I was so ready to stand on the pseudo-stage again. Oliver's in there, somewhere! Could we show the class this time? I was going to try.

I chose Mia's speech from *The Princess Diaries*, from when she formally accepts her princessness, finally, after training with Queen Clarisse, played by the timeless Julie Andrews. Anne Hathaway's delivery of Mia, stating she wanted to be Princess of Genovia, was so imprinted in my heart.

I remember memorizing the monologue quickly the day after the assignment was given. I knew it by heart, front to back, back to front, knew it so well. Yes. SO well that I did not feel the need to practice anymore after the second day, because I thought, hey, I got this. Ha! Oh, you poor baby Camille.

We had so much more time left until D-Day, so like the good student I was, I did *not* practice ever again until the day before. I was overconfident. I remember frowning at my classmates or thinking why are they reading so much when it was "easy" for me. I was so confident at the start, I DID NOT read it again. Until grading period came.

So when I read Mia's speech, I was truly unsure like Mia. Like I really DID NOT know what I was saying. LIKE MIA. The doubt was real. And then halfway through the rhetoric, I remembered everything. So I was able to end with a punch. Thank GOSH. But after this I told myself I was never, ever, ever, ever, ever going to be overconfident like this. Ever. Again. I AM SORRY. I AM!

At the end of my speech, my dear classmates were smiling. But at the beginning, I was so, so nervous through every word of it. I was, but because my friends were taller than me, they sat at the back of the classroom, and that's where my eyes went. When they smiled I was reassured. The nerves I had went silent.

I delivered:

"Hi, um...hello. I'm Mia. I'm really no good at speechmaking. Normally I get so nervous that I faint or run away, or sometimes I even get sick. But you really didn't need to know that...

But I'm not so afraid anymore. See my mother and father helped me by telling me it was OK, and by supporting me like they have for my entire life. But then I wondered how I'd feel after abdicating my role as Princess of Genovia. Would I feel relieved, or would I feel sad? And then I realized how many stupid times a day I use the word 'I.' And probably all I ever do is think about myself...sorry, I'm going too fast. But then I thought, if I cared about the other seven billion people out there instead of just me, that's probably a much better use of my time.

See if I were Princess of Genovia, then my thoughts and the thoughts of people smarter than me would be much better heard, and just maybe those thoughts could be turned into actions. So this morning when I woke up, I was Mia Thermopolis. But now I choose to be forevermore, Amelia Mignonette Thermopolis Renaldi, Princess of Genovia."

Rain. Whenever I hear it's raining, it's going to rain, or it's raining nonstop, I associate that with a bad day. It goes back to my childhood: it's raining, so most likely my glasses will get wet. It's raining, so most likely my very frizzy hair will get frizzier.

I'm programmed to think, oh shoot, this is another freaking obstacle I have to overcome! But, CAmILLe iT's JUsT RaIN…

Yes. Just rain. But I used to think that way! Gosh, the rain highlights my poor balance, and I don't think anyone wants to see that.

But so? So what? Rain is beautiful. It's nature. It's God's way of saying, hey, it can't be sunshine and rainbows all the time! I gotta make it rain so my plants can grow! So I can HEAL and CLEANSE you guys.

What am I gonna do if that's the weather situation, right?

So I gotta dry my glasses. Put my hair up. Wear layers of clothes until I'm stuffed like a turkey on Thanksgiving. Learn proper balance.

Hey, come to think of it, this is all *not hard*. If it's hard fine, then I admit that! Since it's hard for me, I will go slow.

Put one foot in front of the other. I'll just make sure to avoid the puddles and I'll be OK. I think!

Rain. Water. Beach. Does it make sense that everyone around me loves the deep blue sea and I tend to hang back? You mean to say I have to LEARN to love you?

Learn. Learning. Not something I'm good at.

Darn this thing called life.

One of my good, great friends in college, Clarie, asked me once when we were grabbing dirty ice cream, "Camille, how come you're so funny, how did you get so witty?" Well, I told her that I have scenarios and scripts in my head, and she said, "But isn't that sad? So you think of what the other person is gonna say? Shouldn't you not know so you can react...naturally? What if the other person doesn't say what you think they're going to say?"

My head hurt from the conversation—actually it hurts at present, thinking about it—so we went on our day. I didn't go into detail and explain, and like the good friend she is, she didn't dig into it. She just let me sort of talk it out and talk and talk.

Now what am I bringing to the table? Humor? Stories? The ability to talk to myself? I can't teach my children how to be witty! In the first place, being witty is hard to teach.

Life happens, you take it, you say the lesson out loud, laugh, and repeat. Is that how it is? And another thing you don't call yourself witty, you wait for someone to identify that you are. And then you just are because that's what people perceive you to be.

Wittiness. Really just that? What else? What am I going to pass down? I'm sorry to the younger me. I'm sorry to my girls.

I'm sorry that I'm still figuring it out, that you have to see this weak, co-dependent, inept me. But I'm going to try to be someone you deserve.

I'm going to try for you.

For you, my firstborn, Isla, who has seen everything, who has been my therapy and light; and for my second baby, Mia, who is learning everything with me, my strength, my warrior.

I will try for you both.

And for your dad.

Because I love you.

And I love myself too.

College was colorful. I was excited that I got to tackle De La Salle University (DLSU) days with my cousins by my side. Walking into school with their good energy and bright spirits helped ease my nerves. For once, and I'm being dramatic, I know "*Barrios*" was a good thing. I wasn't at the end of the line anymore. I no longer was the new kid. I never got to see my name on a jersey before, but because they were top performers, I had confidence.

I still wanted to be someone outside of my cousins. I loved them, yes, but I thought, can I make a friend without them? Can I fall into the right crowd by my own choosing?

We were about to find out.

"Hey," I said during orientation. A familiar face looked up at me.

"You're from CSA, right? Me too. Let's be friends."

Like Clarie had a choice. Ha! I took her silence as a yes and we were inseparable all throughout.

(Fortunate for me, unfortunate for her!)

It bode well for me that Clarie had a lot of friends from high school, and they were familiar. Whenever they conversed, whenever they said hi to each other in the halls, well, I said hi too. Even if they didn't SEE see me, I felt connected to them in some way. When they hugged Clarie or made *apir* to Clarie, well, it was a hug and an apir to me too. I imagined it. I MADE myself part of their *barkada*, whether they liked it or not.

For me Clarie was my best friend in college. Thing is I know that I was not hers. Her real best friend for life is, and will always be I think, her bff from high school. I understood that, I liked that actually. I respected that. No harm, no foul. No direct hit. Ha. It was just known, and it was true, and that's why I love and care for them like they have been my own barkada ever since.

I liked being with Clarie so much, and I'm thankful her best friends weren't selfish or turned off or anything. They just...let me be. They let me love Clarie even though they knew Clarie since birth, lol, they never gave me the side-eye.

When Clarie had to go with them, she didn't have to explain anything. She just went with them. Period. I was just happy to have them in my life.

I'm glad we weren't like each other, Clarie and I. Thank goodness we weren't! That's how it is, right? Yin and yang, night and day, that's why there's chemistry, when two things come together and there's a reaction, I think. And she'll never admit this, I think we hit it off so well because I said or did things she didn't like or understand or she was embarrassed of me but didn't say anything. She was just there for me. She just let me be.

Like when I commuted for the first time. I was so out of breath by the time I got to her, and in retrospect I was just DRIVEN to the shuttle area, and all I had to do was line up and ride inside. Hello, Camille? What is so hard about that? Another time I left physical education (PE) in a wheelchair. I drowned in swim class. I accidentally swallowed too much water and didn't want to tell the teacher what happened because we were doing synchronized swimming and I didn't want a bad grade.

What was happening? I was all over the place. It was a whole mess in college. But Clarie didn't say anything. She even asked her boyfriend to come get us at the pool because "something happened to Camille," hahaha, and he needed to come stat to push me out. Push me. My gosh.

I was pushed out in a wheelchair with no real sickness (except a headache) from the sports building through the "cool kids" area, past my crushes, and past the girls I wanted to be.

What a nightmare. I remember. OMG, I can't go on. I have to check my pulse.

I think Clarie knew something was "off" with me, but she never rolled her eyes or anything. She was just calm and cool, and she never commented or asked, she just let me figure out the storms inside of me by myself, and when I was ready and needed a break from my own self, she always offered ice cream.

I like that the boys liked her. When they would come up to Clarie and flirt or crack a joke, their attention was on HER, not ME, and it helped me. It helped me open up and be myself. I knew I could not mess up or embarrass myself because they tried to impress her, not me, and I liked that. Instead I got to observe. I got to see who was good at the game and who was so-so. I got to read signs, and even if I misinterpreted anything, it didn't matter, because I was not the object of affection anyway!

I pondered if I would find love in the hallways, and she reassured me that the right person would come when it was time, not to worry. Maybe he wasn't here. She said that he would find me.

Clarie helped me so much academically through college, and I always joked that if it wasn't for her, I wouldn't have survived. She always replies,

"No, Camille. It was all YOU."

I wanted to be something, do something outside of Clarie. We were always together. College, *na*—what could I do myself? What did I have for me? Again it wasn't that I didn't value our friendship, but I needed to learn how to stand alone. Was I still going to pass without Clarie? Did I have a voice of my own?

I think I did. I did have a voice, but what did I know? I couldn't do anything with JUST a voice.

I had a classmate and friend, Marika, who was a DJ for our school's radio station, *Green Giant FM*. That year they were on the hunt for the next batch of fresh faces with new voices. She encouraged me to apply. I was doubtful at first, because I never did anything like it before. Rika said that it was going to be fine. She said I had a nice voice, and it would be better if I had some control, lol! She also thought I was funny, and she had a feeling her DJ-mates would like me. Rika said it would be a chance to meet new people too.

I said OK, why not? If I didn't make it, I would still have at least one friend, right? I would still have Clarie.

So I entered. I did. Music plus talking? Say no more, I AM IN! That was the perfect extracurricular for me.

Never had I put myself out there before. The weekend workshops, training sessions in the sound booth, impromptu speeches, pop culture quizzes. For training they paired me up with a fellow trainee at random, and on the spot, we had to work together to make a radio show.

It was so fun. Brought back so many memories from childhood: our impromptu performances, musical shows, dance numbers. Finally instead of being shy and unsure of myself around others, I felt relaxed and safe.

The music did it. Maybe it wasn't S Club 7 or Backstreet Boys or Celine Dion, but it brought me back so much, I was able to move forward.

Judgment day came soon enough. It was the final round. The panel was only picking ten.

While waiting I remember feeling excited and hopeful because Rika was a judge. I thought, well, that's good news already, right? Shoe in? Not yet, Camille. Rika was only one out of five. She was one/fifth, so who knew what the others thought. She could comment, maybe even sway them, but the final decision was not hers alone.

When she came out of the room, she was smiling. She walked up to me. Eyes forward. I felt the confidence already. Rika and I are the same height, lol, so the power in her eyes transferred well to me.

"You made it!!! You're in, Camille!!!" Rika exclaimed and we embraced for so long.

"OMG, I did?! I made it?" I didn't believe this was real. I was about to jump when,

"But," Rika began, and her tone turned serious, "There is a BUT, Camille. You almost didn't."

My heart broke. A mix of emotions. Was I prepared for what she was going to say?

She said, "They liked you, and they want you on air, but some didn't think you were ready. Someone commented that you talk too much."

I inhaled sharply. Good dose of constructive criticism. The first of many.

Rika didn't hold back:

"Camille, yeah, you have the accent, but honestly no one's gonna wanna hear you if you keep going on and on and on."

I winced. Yes, I do remember what she said to me, because it stung. I couldn't slap her or shut her up even if I wanted to; she was a judge!

"Too much talking and you'll be annoying on air. You have to have a balance. You'll learn it. You can. They like you. They know you can. Just control your levels."

I was going to say something, but I thought about controlling my levels already.

She went on, "One of the judges was close to saying 'No,' but I made them realize that look, Camille can practice her levels and learn how to do it right. She can be trained. But you will never find another Camille. Give her a chance."

Tears were in my eyes.

"Promise me, you'll work on it," she said.

Twelve years later, I'm still working on it.

Challenge yourself to be better than who you were yesterday. You're only in competition with yourself. Well, isn't that the best thing you've heard all year?

If that's the case, then the only voice in your head that matters is yours, anak. Let your own voice be light, singsong, uplifting, forgiving, encouraging. Those are the voices you have to listen to.

If you have doubt, just start with loving yourself. Believe and love yourself and know yourself truly, and you will find your own answers in time.

You will know your own voice. Is there another voice inside your head, baby? Let me speak to them after school.

I'm not saying to not listen to others' opinion and advice. Please be open to that. But if those opinions are negative, if they bring you down, if they're not cheering you up, then it's OK. Let the words fly by. Smile and take it, I know you can handle it. Don't let those words crush your beautiful spirit.

On days you feel slow, like you've had enough, like the world is too much or maybe "I" am being too much, just breathe. Slow down. There's always tomorrow.

I'm not perfect. Your dad sure as hell is not perfect. He may be your favorite, but he's not perfect. Unless someone can show me a tangible award with the words engraved that they are perfect, then don't feel any pressure. Let's not give ourselves that pressure because life is all the pressure we need.

I'm not a dog person. It's not for everybody! I was sensitive and allergic growing up, so now I automatically stay away.

Never really cuddled with a doggie, and I just don't see myself sleeping with them in bed at night. Does that make me a horrible person? Of course it doesn't.

Isla's a dog person. She says she only likes one so far. Henri's a dog person. Every dog on the street might come if they're called here.

So I'm around dogs, whether it's my favorite thing or not, and you know it's a-OK. I'm not gonna change my taste—that's me, I never was a dog person, but I'm not going to distance myself either if they're there and I'm speaking to family or friends.

Seeing dogs with my family members and knowing that I'm not a dog person is healing. It's like I don't LIKE like you, but I LOVE you.

I can't be near you because of the reasons I stated above, but I care for you, and I love seeing you bring my family joy.

It's not my preference to rub your belly or scratch behind your ears, but I love how you look at me with questions or when you wag your tail at me or when you automatically stay away from me because you know how I feel without me having to say it out loud…because of all of that, I love you even more.

Something about me not being a dog person makes me believe that I am, in fact, a dog person. (Don't mention that to anyone I live with!)

Music is my constant. Husband gone for seven months? Music. Wake up alone at 5 a.m.? Music. An attempt to do ONE push up? Music. Sad news? Soft, solemn music. Celebration? Music. Solo photoshoot? Music.

I hear music, it sets the tone. The mood. Walking down the aisle, music. Commuting, music. Writing, music. In the zone, music. Family gathering, music.

It's free! Just press play. If there's no device, no problem. I recall the song I heard yesterday or last year and I'm good. I think we should always sing to ourselves sometimes, or if we need absolute quiet, just have it in our heads.

Now, what KIND of music? That part is relative. I decide what I like, what helps me survive.

You can imagine how I thrived as a DJ and gave it my all. I had so much to say, so many stories to share. Seeing a microphone was incredible, but like Rika said, slow down, calm down. Know your levels. Balance. Listen to the audience.

Audience. That's right. I'm here to play M-U-S-I-C, not speak about myself and my background and go on and on and on.

They don't want to hear Camille speaking all the time, maybe they want to hear the M-U-S-I-C, the very reason they're even tuning in?

There's the awareness. Finally. I was fortunate to be in the DJ seat. But remember, Camille, you have an audience. A responsibility. If you don't listen to your audience, you end up crafting a playlist that only sounds good to YOU. That's great, right? Music you like?

WRONG.

We're on air, a live station, people are listening to you not just to hear you, but they want to hear music that is popular, music that they enjoy. Fine they may agree with your tastes, but that doesn't mean they want to hear your set over and over. If that's the case, then I would have played BSB, Usher, Justin Bieber, Chris Brown, Mariah Carey, Celine Dion, ABBA, Avril, Britney, Christina, Rihanna, Coldplay over and over again, you know?

No, Camille. Listen to your station bosses. Listen to your audience. Research on what's popular. Take note of the banned songs. Understand what other people like. Understand that some songs may be hits with you but not with others. Also the other way around.

Take that all into consideration. Once you do mix it with your own list, your own spin, then BAM, we've got ourselves a live one.

Today it is very hard for me to last fifteen minutes in a conversation without attributing what the other person said to a song I once heard. Or maybe there is a lyric that has been playing in my mind over and over, and I can't help but self-destruct into a song number. Apologies to anyone in my path that is forced to hear me sing or talk about music!

The first thing I ever wrote was entitled *The Garden of Eden*. I remember I was seven–eight because I did it in class. It came to me, and I just had to write it down. Back then I thought it was a groundbreaking masterpiece! But, alas, just words. Still it was my first time to compose anything and write it down on paper. I needed someone to see my work.

What about my class? No, I was too shy to show my classmates or teacher in Encino. What if they laughed? What if they didn't say anything?

What about the people in my home? No, I didn't want to show them. I was around them all the time, so I thought if my writing was bad, I'll be reminded all the time it was bad. I'll be embarrassed. I'll think about it too much.

I needed fresh eyes, another opinion. Maybe an adult I didn't live with? I was looking for some validation. Encouragement.

The Garden of Eden. It was about a girl with long, straight black hair who was so lost in the—you guessed it—Garden of Eden, lol. She was lost, and the place was beautiful, and she had so many questions and was questioning life, and I remember at the end I wrote, "Was there a God? Is He real?" something like that. Gosh, I was so proud. I thought it was very deep and rebellious of me.

I read it to Nang-Nang. I remember holding my breath as she read with squinty eyes through her thick glasses. At the end of the short story, she said,

"Oh, it's good, Mim! Keep it up!"

Those words. Really?

I knew then I wanted to be a writer. A storyteller. Anything with words.

Then 9/11 happened, and I was fascinated by the news and stories and people on the scene. The event was, yes, a tragedy, but my ears were focused on the reporting. The announcements. The updates.

I wanted to be a journalist.

I kept diaries, journals, notebooks with short stories. I'd write chapters on Microsoft Word and make up names and dates and stuff I guess I wanted to do. I'd write stories of Betty and Veronica, and I'd copy paste the comics but in letterform. I'd continue their story with Archie and the gang.

I wanted to take writing classes. I wanted to know there were other storytellers out there, but then later I realized…wait, writing? Isn't that just a subject in school? It can't be a job or a talent or something you do forever, right?

So I didn't make my interests a priority. I didn't speak up when people asked me what I wanted to be when I grew up because, well, I wasn't going to be anything but just "Most Improved," so I wasn't going to say it at all to save myself the trouble.

Wrong thinking again!

I tried to go after it once. I did. I took journalism as an elective in fourth year. Entering college, literature was my first choice. I decided that I wanted this, I did. I wanted to continue what I left behind.

But something, a voice, was mocking, telling me I wasn't going to make it. "Literature is just reading and writing. Why would Camille need a degree in that?" the voice said. So I listened. I allowed myself to be swayed by my own doubt and fear. I traded my interests, my passion.

I made some changes. And mind you I don't regret a single thing about those changes. If it weren't for a switch, I wouldn't have had a certain English class, and if it weren't for that class, then Henri wouldn't have found me outside of the class, and we wouldn't have shook hands that might as well could have shook the whole Andrew building.

See. I have no regrets.

No regrets about college or the decisions I made. Just a deep ache for that younger me. A small pain because literature was what my heart wanted, but I caved and gave in to my brain.

I wish I was stronger back then.

I wish I knew how to say what I wanted.

Yes, everything happens for a reason, and I have no regrets. No one to blame.

I am just giving a tight embrace to the younger me.

"Mom, what's an antihero?"

"It's a hero but something is wrong with him or her I think. I'll research later. But from what I remember, they're flawed and they make mistakes, but for some reason, the audience loves them anyway and wants to see them win."

"Oh, like you."

Thanks, my anak.

But see that thinking is so wrong. EXACTLY what was wrong. Since I was around music so much, it BECAME me. Like I became it. I did not know how to separate. I saw myself as the lead in music videos, as the main character, as the one singing front and center all the time.

No. That doesn't fly when you're interviewing for jobs. When you're out in the "real" world.

There's no music. There's no soundtrack.

Only real life.

I brought up that I was a DJ in just about every job interview I had. It was a conversation starter. I had no other extracurricular thing or identifying mark about me. I sadly did not have stellar grades to show

51

off and I didn't volunteer anywhere newsworthy. I was so nervous coming up with a résumé because I had nothing to impress interviewers with.

All I know is that I had my voice and my energy. All it took was one person to hear and see it.

That person was Tori.

"Good grades," one of the first things she said. I remember that because like heck I had good grades—HA! So why in the world would she say that? Was she being nice, was she teasing me, or maybe testing me to see if I'd agree or disagree?

"I tried my best in classes," I said, "I didn't come out as the best in any of them though. I love writing."

I was the scriptwriter for my thesis film, BUT our group did not graduate on time. Because I didn't want to explain why, I didn't mention it.

"Good. We do a lot of writing," was her comment. I couldn't read her. Stoic. Firm. No emotion. Can't budge!

"And I was a DJ in school. I like talking."

I laughed nervously at myself and hoped it translated well. Fingers crossed. Did it work?

"I see that. Good. We need your energy." Tori offered a smile. The rest is history.

I made colleagues and friends, and I enjoyed the flashy, fast-paced environment of the small but mighty public relations company. Because it was too fast paced at times with a lot of moving parts, I didn't get to address my own personal situation, the fact that I still lacked self-confidence, self-worth, and independence.

Well, I thought that could wait. I don't want them to see me unpack my baggage. My work family, the people who voted me as "Miss Congeniality," I won't let them see my dark side, fears, or weaknesses. I was trying to show up as a bright, confident PR newbie, and I didn't want to rock the boat.

In braving the waters at work, I put my self-development and self-reflection on the back end. I promised I would get to it later, but working on myself became less and less of a priority, and the days just got too fun for me to want to go back to the truth of myself. I mean let's be real: Yahoo! OMG! Awards launch versus learning to love myself.

Duh! Awards please. I can learn about myself later.

Later.

Later.

Later Tori moved on to another company. We kept in touch, and she mentioned an opening on her team.

If Tori saw me once, she would see me again. I was going to show up this time. I was going to show her I learned something.

So I applied.

Ogilvy Public Relations Manila is a company of giants. Company of giants. That's what they say! And yes, that's what they ARE! Company of giants. It was a great call back to college, *Green Giant FM*, and I hoped and prayed.

I'm talking global scale. I couldn't be or act all over the place here. No. I had to be better. And the place was perfect. The perfect mix of glam and intellect. It was HOME away from home.

I was excited and looking forward to seeing Tori again, of being interviewed by her.

But it wasn't Tori. It was Martin. And one quick gaze over his smart attire and sharp movements and I knew I was in for it. Something told me my charms weren't going to work here.

"Camille?"

I stood up and fixed my hair, windblown by the Makati traffic. Darn, there goes the Sunsilk commercial I was going for.

"All the conference rooms are occupied, so let's do this outside."

Score! Interview on the terrace where I can breathe fresh air. Maybe this would help me relax a bit.

"So Tori referred you," he started, and I remember feeling proud already.

Wrong. Calm down, small fry.

"Taga DLSU ka din?" he said, putting me at ease.

I said, "Yes, I went to the one on Taft Avenue." He picked up that I wasn't from here.

"Oh, hindi ka nag Filipino? So how do you talk to media? How do you plan on communicating with your client if they're representing a Filipino brand and you're pitching to Filipino media?"

OMG. PA-TAY *kang bata ka*. I thought, Tori, where are you? I'm sorry! I had no idea what I was doing! Why did she bring me here? Why did I apply? Tori? I'm sorry; this is all a mistake!

I did not answer him. I left him hanging. It was the worst. Earth, just please come and swallow me whole. We were outside, on the roof, he could have flung me off the twelfth floor if he wanted.

But he didn't.

"OK. Media question," he began. Please, I am so, so, so thankful he talked again and gave me a chance to redeem myself.

"You have an event. It's your event, and you're leading the team. You're briefing the client. Telling him what to say, what not to say. You're coaching him on his speech. There's media at the front door. They won't be allowed inside unless you let them in. They're giving your name. They need to be let inside. You're with the client. What do you do?"

I froze. I've done this a hundred times before, so why didn't I have an answer now? Hello?

I answered, "I excuse myself and say I need to use my phone. But I really go to the entrance to greet media and let them in."

Yes! I have a voice! His expression was so hard to read, I really was on the edge of my seat.

"No. No, no, no, no, no, no. No, Camille," he said, shaking his head. "You NEVER leave a client unattended and alone especially if it's your event and you're their point person. Their guide. Camille, we're a TEAM. Remember you're with a TEAM. Use me. Call me or text me or call Tori or text Tori and tell her, 'Hey, I'm with the client. Media XYZ is at the door looking for me. Please get them.' Oh, see, tapos!"

"Ooooh yeah," I said, and he gave a shadow of a smile. Or was it my mind playing tricks on me?

My memory fails me as I try to recount that second question he asked me during the interview. I know, I KNOW he asked me a second one because I got it right the second time, and that concluded our chat outside.

"I see myself in you, Camille," he told me, and I didn't know what to say to that. I just smiled as much as it was professionally possible to do so.

He then handed me some papers and asked me to write a press release. The topic was a new product was about to be launched by a tech client they were handling. I was supposed to write the press release slated for the event day.

He only gave me ten minutes and said, "Just write what you can." When I was done writing, he looked at my sad, sad article (which didn't even have a title) and said, "Nice. We'll call you if you get it."

Dismissed.

I went down the elevator with my head held high but less and less hopeful with every step I took toward the exit. Right at the lobby, my phone rang. I remember. Me and the receptionist had an eye-to-eye moment.

"Camille? If you're still here, come up. You have another interview."

I flew, gosh, I FLEW to their office before anyone could call back and say they made a mistake! Upstairs they said that Martin liked me. They said that the bosses trusted Martin's judgment.

"He what?! That was him LIKING me?" I wanted to cry tears of joy. If he didn't swing the other way, I would have had an office crush.

"Martin handles tech and sports. The guy you will be replacing knows a lot about both subjects. Do you know anything about tech or sports?" I was asked.

I told them how much I loved Kobe and the National Basketball Association (NBA). But that was all. I never played. I just knew the game.

"Great, go head on to HR."

As we approach the month of love, I reflect on the thirty days that have passed. I see a pattern in my ramblings. Words frequently used:

God. Fear. Doubt. Embarrassed. Lack. Most Improved. Try. Trying. Self-love. Self-worth. Confidence. Growth. Family. Music. Classmates. Family. Stories. Light. Beautiful. Energy. Love. Laugh. Healing. Warrior. Strength. Game.

It's been thirty days of candidness, true fear, salty tears, and insane laughter. I love what these exercises have done to me. I love that I'm reconnecting with myself and with people mentioned in some of these stories. I feel comforted by my own words.

I find strength knowing my weaknesses. I like reading back and actually disagreeing or shaking my head at some parts. I like that I see my poor judgment, and I love my naïve, young self.

To think that was just yesterday. Something admirable and misunderstood about the former me, can't help but chuckle.

I do have a long way to go, but at least I set myself on this path of self-discovery. I feel like I don't ever want to go back to the old me who was so clouded.

I don't want to go back to the me who had no voice.

Guess I have to rise above my own self-doubt and worries and be somewhat of an alpha and kind of prove that to…to who? My pack? Or to myself?

Sometimes the best way to go about your days is to be silent but sure of yourself—and that's what I am now. Not yet a lion or alpha, but in a way I'm a bit more sure about myself.

To the other alpha snoring next to me, well, I'll see you in the ring. Bright and early.

Being honest with myself means I have to face the embarrassing, weak, angry, loose, unkept parts of me. It's not a territory I am comfortable with.

It's not always a pretty picture. But someone pulls me into the light whenever I need to be pulled through.

That someone deserves my time, love, respect, honor, and commitment.

I am starting the year with His words and His story. I am asking Him to help me with mine. He may not give me the answers today or tomorrow or next year, but He'll show himself to me in His little but great ways.

I'll be here to see and listen to Him.

We will.

One day you could be listening to the Spice Girls on a Sony Walkman and the next you are launching the company's latest gadgets in an upscale location in Manila, surrounded by renowned media and personalities.

If all you do is literally sit in the meeting without speaking, taking notes while the smart minds trade ideas, that's great. If all you do on a Friday night is print and wrap gifts until midnight, that's great! If all you do is make one PowerPoint (PPT) presentation, wonderful. Let's kick it up a notch—let's say you present the presentation.

Out loud.

To your leader.

And to the team.

Add in more team members to that meeting.

Invite your **boss** to that briefing.

Let's say everybody has finally given you the floor to speak, and you realize that this is the part you so desperately asked for all your life. Will you be ready?

I think so. I think you will.

If you know what you're talking about, anak, and you gave everything you had into those slides, you put your time, effort, honesty, energy, and happiness in that PPT, then there's nothing to be scared of.

Nothing.

If you love what you're talking about, and you're with a group of people you admire and respect, even if you make a mistake when speaking or don't know the answer right off the bat, then it shouldn't be a problem. They're not there to judge you, make fun of you, or belittle you. No. They're there to love and support you. They're going to help you shine. They're there to give you that confidence to your doubt. If you slip they will help you, ready with a first-aid kit, they won't break you even more.

You. Got. This.

Imagine that my very humble and first-grade presentation starts, beginning, middle, FAQs, done. Cut to more planning and brainstorming.

After the presentation everyone went on their busy day. But Omar stayed behind. I saw him turn to me for one second. I knew it was coming.

Here we go with the feedback.

To my sheer surprise, it was not what I was expecting. Omar said he liked everything I presented and—this part hits me so dearly—he liked the WAY I presented it.

Omar said he learned something.

Learned something…from me?

He said he liked hearing me deliver my presentation. He said, and I will never forget because it was such a shocking compliment:

"That was a great presentation, Camille. I can see how…different and confident you are now. I'm impressed, and I am happy for you. Good luck in your event."

Those words. Uplifting words. I heard loving words like that once before.

I couldn't have made that moment up. Please don't take that from me.

Omar and his words left such a deep impression on me. To this day it helps me keep going.

One, come on, he has been thru hundreds of presentations with smart teammates, so I'd assume that one second of seeing me, he could easily compare and contrast. He sat through my presentation from beginning to end, and he had this critique? And he didn't keep it to himself? Gosh, I am so, so thankful he let me know. How big of him to let me know without gaining anything in return.

He's a senior to me in the field. He could have thought, oh, I know this. I don't need to be here! I know what a media event is. But no, instead it was let me listen to this new kid, she's got something to say.

Yes, we had a good event. I mean I think we did. I'm not sure about the numbers or the impressions, but to me it was a good event.

We ALL worked on it. Team effort. But gee, this was something special to me because I finally presented something I loved, I got to share my voice that once upon a time I was so scared of, I actually made sense sharing my thoughts, I talked about what mattered to me, and the team didn't laugh. I made my ideas known and no one made fun…that meant so much to me. It did.

Even my boss, Leah, asked me for direction. She asked me what she was supposed to do. She asked ME to give her a role. She asked ME for talk tracks, she asked ME for guidance on what to say if the client or media had a question she had no answer to.

Leah asked me…for MY opinion? She's led international launches, campaigns that span years, briefings with CEOs and presidents and managers, and meetings on top of buildings and skyscrapers…and she asked…ME?

"Camille,
What
Should
I
Be
Doing?"

Me, little me. Me, Miss I-don't-know-how-to-do-anything-because-I-have-low-self-esteem-and-I-constantly-laugh-at-myself-instead-of-facing-the-truth, me. And then she ASKS me for direction? She wants to know what I think?

The humility. The pure love and respect. Thank you. That is why I'm so honored to come from a company of giants, and I will never forget the impact they have made in my life.

I will always be proud of my background and how the "giant" chose to take a chance on the little guy—I mean GIRL.

Don't get me wrong. Yes, I had friends in LA. Good people. God led me to the right crowd. Good and kind. There was the occasional bully, but kids will be kids. We got through it. Even then I saw good people who loved me for me.

It was all…me who felt like I didn't belong, like I wasn't worthy to "hang out" with. Like it made no sense to have me around.

I felt like it was a problem for me to have friends. Oh, but why, Mimi?

Since I didn't have a permanent place to sit during recess and lunch, I wandered. I felt like I didn't need to be with a group. I felt my presence was not necessary, so I just removed myself politely. I felt like I didn't belong.

So I thought of places I could go for lunch or recess. Bathroom? No. Eating there was unsanitary. I already tried it once and did not appreciate the extra ladies' room commentary.

Locker room? No. Sweaty.

Nurse's office? Again? No. They will ask me again why I'm sick and would call my home.

Library. That's it! Library. I could hide there, and at the same time I'd look smart. Ha. Hopefully that would paint me as the ever-so studious one.

While browsing I stumbled upon Edgar Allan Poe's collection, and it was good timing too because we were reading a lot of him in class. So to pass time and catch up, I thought, let's read some more.

"The Raven," *The Tell-Tale Heart*, *The Cask of Amontillado*, *The Mask of the Red Death*. Honestly some of the words and paragraphs ran right over my head because of the advanced vocabulary, lol, and a lot of it was psychological and too much for me to comprehend. The puzzle of words was too much for me to solve.

But even so I kept reading. I liked how the author could paint pictures with words. I liked how, even if it was suspenseful or scary, I still was so captured by the darkness…I saw it happening. I was so drawn. Like I didn't understand the words, but I FELT the words. It was so real to me, I loved how the author did that so easily.

I made a promise to myself to finish all his literary works first. His major ones at least before I started on others, just so it wouldn't get overwhelming for me. Then I read something of his, *The Purloined Letter*, and there was a part I didn't get, so I stopped.

I stopped reading Poe. I stopped reading altogether. Ha. Where's the promise? What happened? Why?

Why did I give up so easily? If I just learned what the words meant. If I just tried a little more. If I just kept reading. Come on, Camille, you're in a LIBRARY. If you don't get it, just ask and someone will know! You DO know there's a dictionary somewhere in here, right?

Well. That's that.

So today if someone were to ask, have you read any good books lately? Or who's your favorite author? What's your favorite book? I won't have a straight answer, but I can offer this lengthy story instead, lol.

I admit I don't read. I haven't read in a long, long time, and I'm sorry for the reader I once was.

So how are these words coming out right now? How am I able to compose when yesterday I couldn't even speak?

I think when you spend so much time alone or observing others, you pick up on things. Details. Mannerisms. Other people's way of speaking. You see or hear things you like, copy them. Something you disagree with, stay away from it. Know it, but let it pass. No need to be hostile, just let it be if it comes and goes. That's how these words appear. So am I just a copycat?

I write about what I see or hear. I react to others and write it down.

Are these words really from me?

How long is the average song? Three minutes, three and a half? That's how long it takes for me to determine how I feel about a track.

First fifteen seconds of a song, I can tell if I will like it or not. Not if it's a HIT, I can only tell if I'll like it after fifteen seconds. Like that Death Cab song with the long intro. Anything by Dua Lipa works. Earth, Wind & Fire, no brainer.

What's the average time it takes for me to know how I feel about something else though? A person? Situation? Three minutes? Actually I feel less than that. As my favorite webslinger calls it, "My Spidey senses are tingling!"

Less than two minutes to feel good or "off" about something. Less than one minute to understand the fear, doubt, and embarrassing state I'm in.

Less than thirty seconds to fall in love with a person. A moment. A story.

Less than twenty seconds to feel if they're genuine, if they're true, if they're real. Friend or foe.

Less than five seconds to understand their heart. Their energy.

Sometimes my reading is off and my first impression is wrong, and I LOVE that.

I **love** being wrong about a person. I love when they prove me otherwise. I love when I'm surprised, when I find myself scrambling, when I realize the script in my head is WAY off.

Three instances I was proven wrong:

Marion.

Kim.

Henri.

First Marion. I've shared that my first choice of a major was literature. So was his. We were always grouped together and found ourselves in the same circles. Ha. I remember when we first met, there was this dude in a red polo shirt, sitting cross-legged outside the class we had together. Chin resting on his hands in a praying position pa, lol, *akala mo*, deep in thought, *yun pala*, he's just thinking of his next curse word and story! I thought that I was early, but look at this guy.

I saw it immediately; he was a storyteller too. I picked up that he was making people laugh with his corny and offensive jokes. This particular day I saw him, I remember cringing and thinking how bold of him to curse so coolly. It was then I saw how you can express yourself like that but mean absolutely no harm. It was just his style as a storyteller.

I respect that, I like it. It is appealing to me until now. He showed me you can be foul in your words, but if the story evokes emotion, then there's no warrant for your arrest!

His crude humor was a hit with everyone who passed by. People flocked to hear him; they paused to listen not because his stories started with a "*Tangina*" or whatever, but because what he said after was actually interesting. I saw that. I didn't understand it, he spoke too fast, but I SAW that. I FELT that.

I was threatened by that, lol, because HEY! I'm a storyteller! That's all I've got! Don't take it away from me! That's my THING! Please!

Marion was so opposite to what I knew. He continued speaking and cursing so fast in Filipino, and yet people were so drawn to him. I was too, not in a romantic way, but I knew he was a real one. He had that energy. That likable candidness. The transparency and no shame.

I wanted to be around that boldness, certainty, and entertainment.

But WHO was he? Should I even take the first step? I was not going to. So he did. He first introduced himself to us, and I remember making a mental note: Gee, I will NEVER end up being close friends with this guy.

Well. Never say never.

Marion spoke at our wedding. He delivered the most heartfelt poem that Henri and I will forever be grateful for.

Second Mary Kimberly. When I started working in PR, I fell down the rabbit hole. Everything was dazzling and dramatic. The movement. The craziness. The emails. The invitations.

The hours were long, and it was tiring being in heels all day (OMG, heels?! That seems like a CENTURY ago), but I loved it because there was never a dull moment. Someone, if not me, was ALWAYS talking, laughing, or telling a story, so it was a dream come true.

I found myself liking my voice, a voice different from DJ Millie's, and for once, for once, the spotlight was on me, and people saw.

Then one day my teammate mentioned that a former intern would be starting with us, she'd be on board as an employee. My first thought, great, the more the merrier!

Cut to Kim walking in. She had her own office *agad*. She talked fast, looked pretty, was tiny and cute (like me?) but one upped me in so many ways—long straight hair, fashion sense, knew all the "in" celebrities and media, was clearly already everyone's favorite. From the get-go. It was Kim.

Oh no. There goes my "Miss Congeniality" crown. Immediately after we met, I told myself I would NOT hit it off with her. We'd never be close.

She had big energy, and I had big energy, so this was never going to work. It's like that, right? When you see someone who is like you but better, you want to turn away. She was magnetic, and I thought I was magnetic, so two magnets, well, they just can't jive! Again I told myself this was NEVER going to work. We are NOT going to get along.

At that time I compared it—see me and Clarie got along because we were opposites, right, yin and yang, she let me be loud while she smiled and solved my problems in silence. Clarie let me talk, oh, but me and Kim? No, no, no.

BOTH of us wanted to talk. BOTH of us had a story to tell. BOTH of us had the same shrill, high-pitched voice that got volumes louder every time there was a plot twist, or maybe that was just me. BOTH of us laughed at our own jokes. We talked OVER each other so many times. Tori had a question, BOTH Kim and I had an answer. The same answer, lol, but we BOTH wanted to reply. In our own way. At the same time. BOTH of us panicked before we even knew what the pitch was.

Tell me how in the world me and Kim became close like we've known each other for years? How did we pull off the Yahoo! OMG! Media event and launch, how did we get home after being stranded in our building, how did we stay sane after hours and hours reading newspapers to each other? How did we make sense of it all when we BOTH did not understand what the contents of the briefing book meant? Someone tell me. I'm not sure; let me call her.

To much of her dismay, I always set her up with my single male friends. In pitching her to them, I'd always say, "Kim is great. She's fun, she talks fast, she's cute and petite, she's like me from another dimension." Lol. Oh man. If I saw myself in music videos, Kim did too. If I was once a DJ, then Kim had her OWN playlist blasting in HER OFFICE.

Kim provided the entertainment at our wedding.

I will pause right here and choose not to write about my other half. I'm not going down the cheesy lane. Our story is not done, so I'm not gonna go there.

What I CAN say is that I'm so very big on first impressions and energy and how people make you feel.

I credit my senses, I do, they come in handy. But I acknowledge that they are not always right, as proven by the cases above.

And there are special instances this does not work. Like with my childhood, I cannot and will not temper with childhood magic. Even if I wanted to, I can't... read the person who passed me the ball. I can't dissect the person who helped me become Oliver. I can't touch the baby who held my actual baby so I could enjoy brunch.

There are some things too out of this world to understand, and I want to sleep tonight, so I won't even try.

I'm not the DJ anymore. Fortunately or unfortunately Isla's in charge now. She chooses the next track. She decides if we listen to K-pop for the whole road trip or if we can add some Disney or Ed Sheeran to the playlist.

We can't listen to music on our way to church. I mean we, yes, we CAN, but like we, me and Isla, literally CAN'T listen because we can't help but sing along loudly at the top of our lungs. Our commander can't take too much of that. He only has two ears.

If we're late, sorry. We have no time to be distracted. But! If we're early, if we're good with time, then why not, let's go. She chooses the song. May fast fact pa about the artist before the song begins.

Today going to church was a blur. You know the morning rush. Coffee, rice, second kid first, first kid second. Wash the dishes, sweep the floor, play their "get ready" music, and hopefully we'll all be inspired to get ready.

Today it was "Anti-Hero" and "Pink Venom." Wonder what it'll be next week.

Three minutes earlier than last time. But last time we were five minutes late. Can Mimi do math? Lol. Still not on time, but HEY. Earlier than last time. So that still counts as progress, doesn't it?

After mass and lighting candles, we took pictures at the altar. Either it's the kids in one picture, Dada and the kids in a picture, or Mama and the kids in a picture. Can't have a photo with four of us in it. Rare, so very rare if we do. That's how it is.

There was an elderly lady praying in the front pew. Kneeling down. Praying. Dressed in all black. Wearing that net on her head (sorry I don't know the proper name for it) and with a few rosaries hanging from her neck.

She looked up at me and asked if she could take our photo so all of us could be in it. Because of her accent, I did not understand right away, I did not know what she was saying. I also did not want to say "What?" or "Huh?" But she didn't wait for me to. She just took my phone and pushed me to my family. Like the kind of push you feel from someone you already know, you know. A push with love.

She knelt down to take our picture. She **knelt down** on the cold, cold cement floor to take our picture. She was older than Nang-Nang, and *she knelt down for us.*

Knelt. To Take. Our. Picture.

That was too much to ask. We stopped posing right away. I went to the senior citizen to get my phone back and help her up at the same time. She thought I was going to just take my phone and leave. No. We helped her up. She was surprised. We kept saying thank you, thank you, thank you until our voices echoed around the church. She bowed to us. Bowed. She bowed to us.

But *who* are we to be bowed to? Why did she? Why? Do we deserve to be bowed to?

Certainly not.

Oh wow. Thank you. Thank you. For the picture. For the moment.

After our pictorial I examined our first family photos of the year.

Great! Not everyone is looking. As usual! But GREAT. I guess I could say other things about the family picture, but why would I? I love it. It's us.

I can't help but see signs and find meaning in everything. Even if it's so ordinary like a window or a Monday, everything is so…powerful. Profound.

I'm inspired by it all.

Every moment.

Thing.

Song.

Phrase.

I can't get over a sentence a person said yesterday or a year ago or when we first met. If it hurt me, it's with me. If it inspired me, it's with me.

My memory can fail, it can be a battle of he said, she said, but the moment…how it made me FEEL? No, that stays. That part is so ALIVE to me.

Even if we weren't close, even if we were frenemies, I am inspired. Like we're all connected. I told Kim what if that's the title of my book, lol. "We Are All Connected," and I'll have Isla draw stick figures around Planet Earth.

Everyone and everything I encounter has a story. I have a point of view to share.

Some may not like it. Which I get. These spur-of-the-moment feelings or flashbacks of love that happen to me, I can't MAKE anyone want them. I can't FORCE anyone to hear them. My storytelling or emotions can be overwhelming. It's not for everyone. I don't mean harm; I just want to share my love and emotion. But I have to be careful and sensitive with whom I share it with. SOME people—and when I say some, I mean my partner—would rather be kept out of this narrative. Ha. I'll try my best. No promises.

I used to be so scared of my own voice, but I'm not anymore. I hope it's not too late to be brave. If I'm speaking my mind and being me, then why should I be scared? Why is there fear if all my Facebook friends are "friends," right? Why should I stop myself from expressing myself if I'm doing it in a healthy and honest way?

Before I hit 'post,' I ask myself once, twice, three times, "Are you sure, Camille? Are you sure you want your words out on social media?"

Why, yes, I'm sure. I'm trying to be better than my negative thoughts. I'm trying not to be scared.

Two things I am scared of: I fear Him, and I fear myself. The darkest parts of me. Other than that who is gonna tell me my words are wrong?

As Aly puts it: "It's your story. You own what happens to you."

Thank you.

Aly Ma. Gosh, just her name itself is intimidating. On my first day at Ogilvy, we were introduced, and I just took one look at her and knew I was out of my league. The way she moved, not showy but certain. The way she talked, not exaggerated but calm, direct, precise.

In an attempt to break the ice, I asked what Aly was short for, and she replied Allison. I said I liked that a lot. It was very feminine and classic. I said, "I think I'll keep that name in mind if I ever have a daughter." You know what she responded to that? Nothing.

NOTHING. *Deadma*.

I think there was a smile. I don't know. I was too busy wanting to delete myself to steal a second glance.

It didn't take long for this realization to come. *Mataas ng IQ ni Aly. Pero si Camille... um. EQ nalang.* Hahahah.

Since there was a clear difference, I took that as me being unworthy. OK, see that misguided mindset? I still had that. Sorry to admit, but I put a wall between me and Aly because I was insecure. She was everything I was NOT and what I WANTED to be a smart, classy, independent boss-lady with great taste. I did not know how to function next to that.

She was already so, so great at her craft and I was not. So I faltered. The cracks just cut wide open. I felt I was never gonna be like her and did not believe I had a chance, so I'm just not gonna...BE. Why did I still think this way? Did I not learn from elementary school, middle school, TWO high schools...COLLEGE passed with this?

I was so scared I wasn't gonna fill in someone's shoes or be exactly LIKE the example to the T, so I did not know how to be like...myself. My own self. This was before the Sony presentation thing btw.

I still respected her but did not respect myself. I did not believe in myself and my work was affected because of that. Aly and I had our fair shares of back and forth, miscommunications, setbacks. I remember hesitating whenever we had one-on-one meetings on my calendar because I wasn't ready. My report wasn't ready; my slides weren't ready. My press release was AL-MOST ready, but the title needed some work. Oh wait, the lead paragraph needed major restructuring too.

But whenever it came down to crunch time, we put our different personalities aside and just did the darn thing. Century Tuna Marathon in Subic, done. Steph

Curry in Manila, done. MMA Connor McGregor and Frankie Edgar in MoA, done. Various Sony launches, done, you name it. It sounds so simple on paper, but when you're in the trenches and going back to back to back and have to keep it together so the client doesn't hear you stutter, wow.

If I ever get myself out of this, if I ever make it through it alive, I know who I'm running to when I need professional advice and perspective.

We were handling the Globe Telecom account. We had two articles to write in like three days. She got one; I got one. Three days later we're BOTH published. Hers was on the left, mine on the right. She even said, I remember this clear as day in Piccadilly pa, "Good job, Camille! You're published. See?" And she flipped the page to my part.

I was so near tears. I wanted to melt then and there. I stopped myself. No. I don't want Aly to clean up if I make a mess. That's not on her. At this time I would have given her a hug or whatever. But no. I read the body language. I kept it light and short. I said, trembling with euphoria, "Nice. Thanks." Behind the scenes though, I was jumping with joy because I got a nice review from ALY MA!

We moved offices, so perhaps the articles got lost in the shuffle. It's OK, I KNOW that happened. I know it. Please.

When I found out I was expecting, she was the first person I called that I wasn't related to. She was. I ask myself to this day, why her? Why, of all the people in my contact list. Friends…cousins??? After my parents I dialed Aly's personal cell. I did. Something told me to.

I remember looking through our Viber chat and seeing how all our messages to each other were about work. Check this, update that, how many media, I'm on PTO, this is due tomorrow, etc. So why in the world did I want to call her first thing when I had such a huge personal bomb?

A higher power knows. Not me.

Yes, this is my take on the conversation that happened. I remember because I was so nervous and scared.

"Aly? Sorry to call on a weekend."

"It's OK, Camille. What's up?"

I couldn't get the words out; I just started CRYING!

"Camille? Oh, what's wrong?"

"Aly. I'm pregnant."

A beat.

"OooooOooooooOoOOooH," was all she said.

I was gasping for air.

"OK, wait, where are you?"

"In my bathroom." I sobbed.

Hahahaha.

"No, I mean are you home?" she clarified. "Are you OK? Do you want me to get you?"

"Yes, I'm home. I'm OK, Aly," I said, and I remember thinking, OMG, I'm not ready to have Aly Ma at my house. Hahaha.

I said. "I just need your help telling everyone on Monday."

"Yes, Camille. You're gonna be OK. We'll do this together."

Aly helped organize my shower. She lured me, tricked me into thinking I was going in for another one-on-one, where in fact it was a ploy to get me downstairs. I was surprised to say the least and, you guessed it, I cried.

Is it any wonder that when Isla started school, her first friend's name was "Allison?"

Mahjong.

Why do I like this game so much?

I can't get chess. I can't get scrabble. I kinda, sorta can get poker but just enough for show and then nah. Sudoku, *kaya pa*.

But mahjong.

It takes me back. Back to when I saw my parents playing with their friends, and I was just a little child on my father's lap. I'd peek at his tiles, run around the table, look at his opponent's, and come back. Ha. As if I knew what the Chinese characters meant.

I remember watching everyone play. Sometimes they'd play for hours straight, no water break, no bathroom break. No other kids but us.

I remember one night I was watching everyone and listening to all the banter about who would win, all up, *siete pares*, all flower, secret. *Pong, chow, escalera*.

The one in front of my dad said he/she would win. I forgot who it was. I just know that person sat across from us. I was nervous for my dad, I said, "OMG! I hope we get this. I hope."

Then it was Dad's turn to *bunot*. He said, "*Eto na*," before he even reached over. Before he got the tile. He felt the tile. He felt it. He kept looking forward with a smile and he felt it. Upside down without even turning it over. He read the card and slammed it on the table for the reveal. "ANAK NG...!"

He declared himself the winner.

Everyone around us opened their mouths so wide with surprise, someone stood up from his chair to check.

Dad laid out his cards and chuckled.

He won. We hugged. The chips rained down from all corners.

That's why I love the game.

Years later in Quezon City, during a family vacation, someone brought out a mahjong set and my heart leapt.

Then my heart duplicated seeing TWO sets! One for the "oldies," and one for the "young ones."

I was truthfully so excited to teach my cousins how to play. Mimi knows something they don't, you know? It was just a game, not rocket science, but I sure felt the confidence boost showing them how to count their tiles.

I was nervous thinking, oh, I hope they like the game. I hope so. Because it's the ONLY thing I know, lol. I was never ever in that position before. And I was teaching mahjong? Gee, what a big deal it was.

And they DID like the game. We ALL did. I wanted to embrace everyone for letting me have this.

Fast forward to the *pamanhikan*. You're telling me my father-in-law is tall, dark, handsome, a family man, fears God, loves adventure, is a storyteller and host like me, has EIGHT siblings, loves Kobe, has THREE children, shares the same name as my partner-to-be, and LOVES the game of MAHJONG too?

What are the chances? Why God, why have you listened to my prayers and led me to him?

Thank you. Just. Thank you. May he rest in peace.

Playing mahjong is different now. Still my fave, but I have two playmates hanging on my left and right. I could have the best hand and keep it a secret, but Isla will out me before I get a chance to say Pong!

Let's see if I still have it. Let's see. One of these days. I just need three other players.

Mrs. Spivak in eighth grade said that writing is a combination of long sentences and short sentences. Sometimes you have to share all your feelings in one sentence and sometimes in the next, you don't share anything at all. You let the reader infer. You let the reader paint his or her own interpretation of the story. If there's a specific scene you need to map out, do it with detail and honest, raw emotion. But don't let all your scenes play out that way. Let the reader write it themselves.

It's hard for me to say anything without going overboard. You know the detail, the volume, the animation, the facial expressions. That's the way I do it. I'm expressing myself. Maybe it's because it took me years to find my own voice. So when I do have something in mind, it has to flow out.

I can't be that way forever. There's a flaw in that. There's something annoying about that. Honestly how did Clarie even STAND me in La Salle, lol. I mean you have to be so TIBAY for that, you know. Why did she stay by my side when all I did in college was belt out Rihanna lyrics and say the same stories over and over and over? As if she wasn't even there with me when it happened. Hello, 95% of my stories have her IN them, now and then, so wouldn't this all be a bore?

We were going home one night after a late class. On our way to the shuttle. I was feeling so grown up, thinking, I'm a commuter now, I can travel by myself. Reality check, I needed Clarie to show me where the line started, hahahah, or I needed her to tell me where the entrance was. Did I not see the sign, did I not see the start of the line myself? Oh, Mims.

Kent came up to us. Familiar face, but he was tall. See to a short, cautious, and insecure person like the me I was, that was an instant threat.

Alarm, alarm! Check your senses! My first instinct was to stop in my tracks when I saw him approaching. I thought, oh, I'm not gonna like this.

But he came with a smile. He came bearing a gentle aura. He came with big-brother energy. So my Spidey senses went away just like that.

He hit me with a fast one, he called me, "Shrimp!" I did a double-take. Are you serious right now? Are we really going to go down this road second week of college, bullying? "What did you call me?" I said, and I felt my spirit come out of my body, lol. Out-of-body experience *talaga* because I never stood up to anyone taller than me like that.

He was about to talk back, he was. I saw. But I saw one other thing. He stole a glance at Clarie. I saw that. Electricity. He retracted. He said instead, "Nothing."

And that was the beginning of it. Our friendship. Cool guy he is. I would have stories to share and he would listen. Just listen. Why? Is it because I had Clarie, is it because we bonded over Marvel and DC comics? It was a mix maybe. The point is he stayed to listen to me. Didn't judge. He was a strong shoulder to lean on. Not literally—I can't lean on his shoulder, he's like five feet taller than me!

When I needed to pause from storytelling, he'd suggest Wicked Oreos or *Left 4 Dead*. Those would do the trick.

I made a promise to Kent just recently. On my journey to discovering why I am the way I am, on my path to rebuilding myself and disciplining my mind, I told him I'd start with the body. I told him I'll do one push up a day this year, every day. Just one. Why not?

Kent said to go for it, maybe do more. Can "more" be three? Haha! But yesterday for the first time in 2023, I did six. Six straight. I never wanna do it in front of my husband because he's gonna make me go all the way. He might draft me a whole workout regime, hahaha, and maybe I'll be so *batak na batak*, you won't recognize me, na. He's gonna make me go lower or "do it right." Ha. So I'll do it my way. And my way is this slow way. But it's OK, right?

It feels good *pala*. It hurts, but when it's now six instead of one, I feel like I can do anything.

Kent and Clarie came to our wedding with two different dates. They sat at the same table, but their attention was, at that time, not on each other. Both had different relationships after that. Both had their own adventures separately.

BOTH are now touring Bangkok together as I write. Together. They made it to each other. I LOVE their love. Sometimes their love consumes me that I have to call and tell them. It's the same idea every time, lol, it's the same stories from college over and over. Now if Clarie heard my stories fifty times before, it's hundred now! I guess not much has changed since college then, huh.

I tell them how much their love inspires me. If one doesn't pick up, I try the other. The other will be on CC any way. I get to tell my story TWICE—same expressions, same phrases, same volume. Different reactions. That's a treat for me.

I was scared to write about them because there's no ring yet, so frankly things could change, but I'm gonna go ahead and call this endgame. I expect an invite to your wedding in the future, hard copy AND soft copy please!

After this I can't write anymore about the future. I don't want to jinx it. I can only write about the past. I can't go too deep into the past because it will affect my present. And I have to LIVE in the present.

At present a very dear one is teaching eighth grade English to her students. I love that she is shaping minds and reminding them of what good stories are. If I were her student, I wonder. Would I pass? Oh gee, on second thought, don't answer that!

Most movies I like now were recommended to me when I was young.

I was recommended *Speed*, starring Keanu Reeves and Sandra Bullock. *Speed* didn't follow our usual theme during movie nights, so I initially thought, no, I don't think so.

I mean it started off scary! At that time I thought, why am I watching a man make threats and whisper on the phone? This is a total 360 from the musicals and talking animals I was used to.

Alarm? But because I was with an audience, I was not scared to watch.

Play the movie from start to finish.

I. LOVED. IT.

I loved it back then, and I love it now. To me it's everything you need in a movie—handsome leads, the strong man and the equally witty and strong woman behind the wheel. The suspense. The moving vehicle. The bad guy. The best friend who isn't dopey but helpful and smart too. The time running down. The build-up. The romance they capitalized at the end. Implied throughout the movie, but it's not the central point or the main driver, so it's not distracting. Family friendly.

No fancy CGI magic or apocalyptic outer-space stuff of today, so I wasn't confused. I got it, haha. I mean I was old enough to know it wasn't real, but then I also knew it COULD be real, and so that made it so relatable. It was overall easy for me to understand, and that's saying a lot, lol.

I rewatch parts of it so it reminds me of that time. I like it so much, I watch the actors' interviews together. I wanted to see who they are off screen. Sandra's short bob, Keanu's chiseled jaw, how nice!

The chemistry is real too. It's so beautiful. A great part of what got me thru the pandemic: BTS and *Speed*. Not even Kobe. Mamba's words help me greatly NOW, but his untimely passing in 2020 devastated me to the core. I couldn't watch anything related to purple and gold when we saw the news. That's the first news I wrote to Henri when he was gone—not how I was doing or how his daughter was faring with homeschool, lol, but OMG, Kobe died.

Wait I'm switching topics. There's more on *Speed*. Tho the actress is happily married now, she admitted to having a crush on Keanu while filming the movie. Guess what when Keanu was told that she liked him while filming, HE then also admitted that HE had a crush on HER back when they were filming too! Nothing ever materialized because both were just so shy and wanted to keep it professional.

How cute is that. How feel good is that! Too feel good! It didn't work out, but isn't that lovely, the fact that they both felt that spark? And their chemistry was real. And it translated!

I'm glad we were introduced to *Speed*. I'm glad that I took a chance. Ended up falling in love with the movie.

Movies are interesting. You know that they're actors playing parts and have to make it real. It's their job.

But WHO are the actors without the movie? Without the script, without the background music, without the green screen and special effects? Are they still as brilliant, impressive, or moving as who they play, or do they just read lines, are they just pretty faces?

You can see who has the chemistry. Who glows. Who makes it look easy on screen. When the camera's not rolling, who are you?

You can tell who really is well spoken and who needs a script. You can tell if an actor really knows what he's doing or if he's just being directed. You can tell if an actor is really proud of his work. The best is when an actor says he can't watch himself in a movie he made ten years ago. Was it Depp who said he can never watch himself in *Pirates*? Penn Badgley has said so, so many times he can't watch himself as Dan in *Gossip Girl*. I understand. Cringe, watching yourself from fifteen years ago, no matter how snazzy and sparkly the setup. Say no more, Penn! You keep doing You.

It's not like I idolize these actors or follow their every move, hey! They follow me whether I like it or not! Ha.

Take the *Fresh Prince* for example. Will Smith. He was my guy growing up. Weekdays, that afternoon block of comedy. Going home on time was so important because if I was a minute late, I'd miss him singing, "Now this is a story all about how my life got twisted upside down…" He jumpstarted my rapping dreams, OK!

The show. The imperfect characters. The family dynamic. The comedy, some lines went right over my head when I was a kid, but since there was a live audience to laugh during the funny parts, I kind of got the joke. The situational comedy. The fact that Will was not the smartest or richest in the family, but he was… the funniest. And he brought people together. How?

He played Genie in 2019's *Aladdin*. To a lot of people's skepticism. Doubt. Fear he was gonna mess up what Robin Williams made iconic.

Well, I was part of the half that was psyched for this. I was rooting for this. Blockbuster fail or not, don't care. Jasmine's my favorite princess. Will made my afternoons in Encino. I was looking forward to this.

Not Oscar-worthy, yes, BUT HELLO, it's Disney! No pressure! It's for the children, not for the trophy! He did it for the kids, and it was great! Now I can watch it with both my babies? That's something! Sorry if I sang all the songs! Sorry if I cried when Aladdin gave Genie his last wish. "My wish is for your freedom?" How selfless and beautiful…?

And come on, comment section. Cut the man some slack. Of course he can't BE like Williams' Genie, that's untouchable! But he was a damn good Genie for our next generation. A beatboxing, charming, soulful Genie all on his own. And I applaud that.

I can't read comments on pop culture anymore. I can't keep up with the times if the trend now is NOT giving someone a chance. People are mad because Ariel has a different skin color in the upcoming movie when in the original she looks like this or that. Come on, can our thinking be a little more progressive? For our children? For the future?

Now I don't want Disney to shut down my account, so I will close here. Gosh, what am I doing? I can't write anymore, I got to attend to Cindy-Mulan-Aurora and Moana-Anna-Miabelle.

It wasn't supposed to happen this way. Going down memory lane was meant for me to HEAL myself, not WRITE about everything that has hurt or inspired me! Now look at this. What have I done? But we all know, once I start, good luck.

I gotta control it. I don't need to air out dirty laundry. No. Instead, like always, when I'm alone, look at the good memories. The moments that made me laugh. The times I was uplifted and inspired. That's what I should be dwelling on. Like ants attacking food. AVOID the bad, messy human, but KEEP GOING for the sweet stuff. Stay in line.

I can't help it. If it happens, I try to turn away, but my eyes see an object that needs to be romanticized. I shut my brain, but there's still a song playing. You know?

"What Do You Mean" by JB was playing when Steph Curry ran up and down the basketball court in Mall of Asia.

"We Found Love" by Riri was playing when I went to Boracay for the first time in a long time.

"Me and U" by Cassie was playing when I walked past the dancers at CSA during their dance practice. I think it was for the cheering competition third year? I saw them and I thought, wow, nice. I don't think I can keep up. But nice song. I like it. I'll download it on my iPod mini, lol, she's part Filipino too. Cassie.

What was playing when Jean and Paco got married? I don't know, I wasn't there, but I called her as soon as I heard news of their engagement and sang Ed Sheeran and we laughed at my rendition of "Perfect". I remembered our good times like it was yesterday.

I had one rule at work:

Never make friends with your co-workers. Don't get too personal, Camille. We are officemates; we're not friends. I remember telling Tori one day when she invited me for drinks and dinner one night. I thought maybe if I made this boundary for myself, they wouldn't see the skeletons in my closet, they wouldn't realize that I can make the progress report for the client but I CAN'T make a progress report on MYSELF.

Truth was, at that time, I couldn't handle my emotions, I wasn't truly mature for my age, I couldn't communicate properly when that's what I was supposed to do, communicate, lol. Wasn't that my major, communications?

I made that "All Work and No Friends" rule very clear early on because I wanted to come off as mature.

Real reason was that I was not. I did not want to get hurt. I was bullied, I had failed crushes, I was still navigating my life and figuring me out, and I had no real sense of myself…so you can see why at that time…I wanted to distance myself. I thought I will not set myself up for heartache. Insert something poetic like "People Always Leave" à la *One Tree Hill.*

Camille in 2013 thought, I will not get attached. I will not show that side of myself to them. I'm not doing this again. Not GOOD ENOUGH to join their crowd. Here we go again. Tired of the pattern yet? I am.

I just didn't see myself making it. I didn't see myself reaching the business goals. I didn't see myself as good enough to handle their future accounts.

See so much thinking of the future. Too much future thinking, I wasn't living in the present.

But there was someone who WAS living in the present.

That someone, well, he caught up to me.

Did I stick to my rule? No. I stayed late, talking the night away. I went against myself and I DID go for dinner and drinks when Tori asked the second time.

They became my—dare I say it—friends, and it made me WANT it MORE. Go to work early. Read the papers. Send out the invites and then call right after I send them. And then if the person didn't answer, I'd text. Or if they replied, "I got it, thank you, Camille," to my email, lol, I'd walk over to Tori's desk literally around the corner and tell her I did it and I'd ask if there was anything else I could do. Eager beaver. I would ask for direction but darn Kim was already on it.

I broke my rule. My policy. I'm glad I did.

I was pulled in by Kim's charms and the fact that firm and proper Tori could take some shots after hours and wouldn't bat an eyelash.

OH-KAAAY, I see! So these people were profesh, but as soon as we clocked out for the day, their PR masks came off. I saw them. They saw me. They became barkada.

We didn't go hard, no, but to me one sip na was badass, hahaha, and I thought, wow, I crossed over to the dark side. I thought, this is major character development, following one night of karaoke and chips with dip. Oh, Camille, you ain't seen nothing yet.

It was a night after some dessert at Ayala Triangle. After reading work stories over some cupcakes and pasta and more and office gossip, we all said goodbye and slowly began our separate ways. But Jean began to cry.

Henri and I stayed. We lingered. We walked around Ayala Triangle with Jean, not knowing WHY she was crying, but we felt like it was our duty to pause for a while. At that time I was thinking, "What do I do, what do I say?" I didn't even ask him to step in or stay.

I didn't need to, he just did.

He said something. Through some sobs she looked up, probably as surprised as I was that Henri was the first to check on her.

It was about her boyfriend. Paco did something to upset her. I was frozen honestly, I was in no position to give bf and gf advice or add some perspective or give my point of view on relationships and love. I mean I was with Henri, right, what did "I" know? Ha! How can I tell Jean, "Everything is gonna be OK," if I myself DON'T know everything is gonna be OK?

I thought, wait, she is my officemate, no, my FRIEND now, I don't want to be insensitive, I don't know the whole story. No clue on how to provide comfort. How can I give advice?

But Henri said something. And Jean replied. Darn, I can't translate because it was in Filipino. But there was some understanding. He continued speaking and she continued replying and there was no more crying and it was a full conversation without me and I thought, WAIT a minute, wait a dang minute, Jean is MY friend and NOT YOURS, lol. You're not gonna be the hero here! I wanted to switch it back to me, so I asked her, "What high school did Paco go to?"

CSA.

Jean and Paco are now Mr. and Mrs. They got married in 2021. Jean **fought** for this love. I'm guessing she *fought for this like the fighter she* IS and showed HIM how to cry. *Tama yan.*

In the words of our media relations go-to, "*Nakaloka ka*, Camille." When I found out about their engagement, I had to call that second. I sang in celebration. Thru tears and laughter.

Jean took my favorite picture of me and Henri. It's the young us on a boat on our way to a secret spot on Cagbalete Island. It's my favorite shot because he's in his element and I'm NOT in mine, but we're together. It's my favorite because for real, *talaga ng talaga na candid ito*, it's not the posed ones we now ask our husbands to capture. Jean took it without me prompting her. She just took it. I guess she saw a lovely moment and she wanted me to have it. Even if she didn't know our story back then—gosh, WE didn't know ANYTHING back then—she knew something still.

She KNEW.

Jean and Paco. *Alam mo na yun.* I can't make a dedication for everyone. It's taxing. *Di ko na kaya.* I'll just call u guys instead. I'm singing, so I hope you read this first so there's a bit of context. If not your wife will fill you in.

"I'm rubber; you're glue. Whatever you say bounces off me and sticks back on to you."

Whoever came up with that saying to ward off bullies deserves a million bucks.

I use it more so now for *mga anak ko* and also when I'm up against my second in command. It works every time. Never seen an army man kneel, I tell ya.

Setting, playground, 2000-ish.

I was the reigning jump rope champ of Encino Elementary. At least I felt I was. We had these yearly sports competitions where we'd rotate around the playground and play games, and at the end of the whole thing, we'd have a very formal ceremony and teachers awarded those in first, second, and third place.

Categories were softball, racing, and jump rope. There were more, but I can't remember.

But what I CAN remember is that in every awarding ceremony, first place for jump rope went to me. Second grade…wow. Third grade…wow. Fourth grade…wow. Fifth grade…no. I didn't place. What happened?

I'll tell you what happened!

The NEW kid happened! Tabitha moved from another school and joined our school and not only was she instantly popular, cool, and sure of herself, she won MY first-place prize!

I was ready to hear my name for fifth grade jump rope, but no. It was Tabitha!

OMG. The ONE athletic honor I had. That was MINE. I had nothing to show off when I went home. No ribbon. No proof. No nothing. All because of TABITHAAA, lol.

I wanted to hate her, I did. I'm glad we weren't in the same class. I was in Mr. Riley's, and I think she had Ms. Siskin (?). If I find her now, I'll call and confirm, lol, and tell her this story.

Gee, I can remember. Did she have a beauty mark on her face too or no? If I were to comment on her looks, I would say she had caramel skin and looked like a cross between Tia Mowry (from *Sister, Sister*) and Pocahontas with short hair. To me.

I'm good to look for her now, but oh my, back then? She was my enemy. And for what? For winning first place? For being better at jump rope than me? Ha. It's OK, it was my thinking in elementary back then. I wanted Tabitha to be a bad, mean, messed-up person, but no. No. She was liked. She was bold. She was sure. Ugh! Said ten-year-old me.

I remember one time there was a fire drill, so of course instead of being calm and collected as instructed, it was CHAOS and all the kids and faculty meshed together. For line-up I found myself behind Tabitha. Behind her. She noticed I was behind her.

And she said to me, "Oh, you can go." That's all. That's all she said to me. She said that so I could catch up to my class, who was already ahead. She GAVE WAY to me because she CARED and wanted me to be included, didn't want me to be left behind. Am I reading too much into this? Maybe.

Point is Tabitha turned out to be...NICE. There was nothing I could see that was wrong about her. There was no reason to fight. It was my own personal demon saying that hey, she's better than me at jump rope. Then that means I HAVE to hate her, lol. Glad I left that thinking when I passed fifth grade.

So when I see or hear people who still think like that, first instinct is to stay away. But I don't. I don't stay away. I STAY. I chuckle to myself. Because that thinking reminds me of fifth grade and the rainbow on the playground cement. It reminds me of how immature I once was and it shows me GROWTH. It reminds me of how funny everything is. We're not in fifth grade anymore.

I forgot her last name. This is too far back to validate. It might just be "another story," sorry to say. If it IS, well, it sure is heckuva fun one.

We left the house fifteen minutes earlier today. Fifteen minutes! This has never happened before.

So what did I do today that helped me get ready better than last week?

Music, low volume ("Family Madrigal").

Less arguing, more listening (BOTH sides).

No social media. No chatting. No live updates. Less phone. Eyes up front.

I did seven push-ups. I did it!

Now gosh. We're not rushing to church. We don't have to sneak thru the back, haha. We can catch the priest's "Good morning." It's nice to see the people filing in pala.

Reminds me of waiting to see my cousins in Our Lady of Grace. Me, wanting to go to church JUST to see familiar faces walk down the aisle in sacristan clothes. Ha! Me, wanting to go to church JUST to sit behind my family and pray as the adults prayed on.

Now I get a second chance to understand His word. I am determined and serious about getting His direction and focus.

We beat ourselves. The family we were last week, we beat. And I'm hoping next week, we will do better. And after that too. So I'll remember what I did today and will follow it for the Sundays to come. Thank you for your help, Lord! Happy Sunday.

Funny things always happen in class. It's the common setting. Since Isla's going to school now, school is always on my mind.

Seventh-grade English. It was my favorite subject, but I remember I cried one day.

We were celebrating our cultural backgrounds and different nationalities, and on that day, we had a potluck. Everyone brought something from their native home; I brought the good ole *lumpia*. Can't go wrong. Classic.

Of course someone brought pizza and spaghetti. Everybody ate that. No one wanted anything else really. I remember walking past everyone's desks and seeing the kids dig in to the delicacies.

I was so excited to show off something from home. My turn.

When I got to the back room where all the food was, I saw the lumpia. Sitting there covered in plastic, presented very well in a tray. All pieces lined up, ready. May chili sauce pa! *Kumpleto!*

I took the tray and walked to the door. Then tears rolled down my cheeks and my throat filled with thorns. Good thing the lumpia was covered in plastic, I'm sure it didn't need any more salt.

I just opened the door a bit and saw everyone laughing and having fun. I thought, if I join, if I bring my lumpia, will they still have a good time? Will they like me? I didn't think so. I cried even more. I put the food back on the counter.

I remember thinking that if I added my share, I would probably ruin their fun. I was OK to stay there in the back. I didn't want to come out anymore. It was fun without me.

I sat there for what seemed like hours. Minutes *lang pala*, lol, and I think someone came to the back maybe to get soda? Or was it the teacher?

Anyway I came out of the storage room and the person who got me out yelled, "Hey, everybody, Camille brought eggrolls!"

And the class yelled back merrily and came up to me and cheered. And they said they wanted one, and they wanted two, maybe more. And someone said I should have taken it out sooner.

I should have. I forgot the chili sauce.

Thank gosh for lumpia!

February.

This month I was so inspired by love. All kinds. All types. All stories.

Fifteen years with the same love, someone who broke up when they were younger but ended up getting married, someone who took more classes to follow their passion and later end up finding their one true love.

Someone who is so in love with life. Someone who is lovingly growing his business. Someone who is growing and working on her body, because she loves herself and no one else matters more than yourself. Your growth. Your mind.

But I learned more about another kind of love. SELF-love. Self-respect. Boundaries. Protecting your heart and peace. Loving your flaws and past versions of yourself so that you're better tomorrow.

I battled so much of this growing up, and I don't want my littles to have this too. I mean they'll have their own stories and adventures, and I can't fight that. What comes comes.

BUT I CAN ensure they will have this self-love. Confidence. Worth. This sword and shield. They won't need to wait for their thirties for it to click. They can head into battle ready and armed, at your service!

I realize that I do love love. And just because the month will be over, the celebration of love won't stop.

No, it's just the beginning.

I was told that my growth and healing won't happen overnight, no, it's a process. No time limit to that. I'm so happy there's no pressure as I work on myself.

Just love.

"Mom, do you think you're a good teacher?" my firstborn asks.

"I can't answer that," I say carefully. "Good teachers don't say, 'Hey, I'm a good teacher! Come to my class!' Only their students, usually when they're grown up na can answer that."

"Well, I think you are good. I rate you seventy. No, eighty."

"That's fair. How can I improve for the incoming class?"

"Be positive. Make less mistakes. Play more, like how you did with me when I was a baby. Wear bright colors. Don't fight with my DEAREST dad. Use better words."

"Better? Do you mean bigger?"

"Oh yes. Bigger words. Not too kiddie for Mia. She can handle it."

"She can?"

"Yeah, she can do it. And if she needs help, like if she needs help, she can ask me. But let her try on her own to understand."

"OK. And how can I keep being there for you?"

"Be more kiddie with me. Because I'm TWO."

Lol. *Tama lang naman*, she will always be my baby!

As I edit I see how many times I keep inserting Filipino words here and there. I even do so more often now when I tell my stories. I can't help it, OK? I CAN'T help switching back and forth, back and forth. It adds layers to my story. Texture. Doesn't it? Don't I sound good?

Sagot: NO, YOU DON'T SOUND GOOD, you sound like an *****!

In my head I do. I sound good. That's why. I sound good switching because I'm making myself sound bilingual and cultured when I am NOT.

I switch back and forth because when I see the person I'm talking to and that person reminds me of home, I want to be HOME. WITH YOU. Like where you and I met. I can't switch back and forth so effortlessly, but I know someone who can.

My Teacher.

Growing up someone made an impression on me if they were taller than me. Well, that's EVERYONE then, ha. So it didn't take long for me to get attached to my tallest cousin, who I fondly called Teacher. He taught me how to climb trees, taught me about basic math, he taught me about farm animals (?), lol, I don't know why that came to mind. I'm sure he taught me other, more necessary things growing up, but I'm not sure what else, *basta*, I know he's Teacher to me.

Even when years passed and I had "real" teachers in my life, whenever I saw him, I always called him my Teacher, just to bring back those memories.

It stuck. Adventure time in the Philippines, "Teacher." Holiday parties, game nights? "Teacher." Back in LA after fifteen years? "Teacher" *parin*. So it makes sense TO ME that his partner and love of his life, in a way, is my teacher too.

Their story is an interesting one. They met, dated, got engaged, got married, had their firstborn all in the span of two weeks. *Parang ganun*. Joke! Of course not. It was like that TO ME. Seemingly. Because of all of the love. That love broke the time and space barriers.

Since they are married, I call her Ate, even though I think she's a few years younger than me. So by the rulebook, I THINK "I AM" "Ate" to her. But since we're here, we don't call each other anything at all. We don't have to. We can drop the honorifics. But I still do. Still Ate to me BECAUSE she is married to my TEACHER.

The night we met, I asked her, "Do you like my Teacher? *Gusto mo ba Teacher ko*?" Hahaha. Cousins' night meant a few drinks here and there, so I asked her twice. Translated pa.

She replied with a shy smile.

That's all she said.

It spoke volumes. I KNEW it then, and I know it now.

After fifteen years I was back in their home. Where we once rooted for the Lakers. Where I once chased a baby around and around, but when we saw them again, the baby wasn't there. Of course not! I realized that he no longer needed to be chased—the girls chase HIM now. Oh, that baby grew up.

But did I?

I want to say yes, but it was like no. Like no time passed.

Teacher asked the kids what they wanted to eat for dinner and they shouted, "CHICKEN!!!" And of course all that was eaten was the *balat*. The meat went to the adults.

Gulp. Were WE now the adults in this scenario? Time, you thief!

Ate and I bonded over the highs and lows of motherhood. It was great reconnecting after so long and seeing her as a mom. When we went our separate ways, we had different priorities back then. It was like we were both now wearing new glasses…different grades *lang*, but we had something help clear our vision.

"*Alam mo naman,* Mims, it's not the same," she was saying mid-chat. Talking about what we do versus what they do. And I interrupted her, I'm sorry that I do that until now.

"I know it's not. Henri comes home telling me he's tired. I'm like YOU'RE telling ME! I've been home all day with *mga anak mo*!"

We laughed in between a few tears. Still she seemed down. I remembered being in that position. I remembered feeling so low.

I didn't and don't EVER want to see it. NOT if I can help it. NOT **on my watch**!

I know, light-bulb idea. Let's make her smile. LAUGH. I started,

"So WHAT if my two kids are dressed in pink? So WHAT if they're NOT wearing matching clothes? *Mas marunong ka pa sakin? Nanay ka na ng dalawa anak ko?* If the answer is no, then OK. *Manganak ka nalang*!"

Laughter. It worked!

"Mims, that's exactly what my mom would say if she were alive!" (Rest in peace.)

The rest of the night went on with swordfights and magic shows. I calmed down. I lowered my language switching and sermons.

Their church wedding finally happened, just this month. Beautiful. Dream come true for the handsome ring bearer and flower girl. Wouldn't have had it any other way.

Thanks for letting me write this. I am so honored and inspired every day.

Talaga every day. They gave me my favorite coffee mug, which says "New Mommy" in front. I'm NOT a new mom, lol, but there's something special about this secondhand cup. Behind it says the passage, "I lie down and sleep; I wake again, because the Lord sustains me." Psalm 3:5.

I stare at it in the mornings I am a zombie and I'm afraid of the day. But then I read the words and there is no reason to be so afraid, so scared, because my Teacher is here. There's faith and wisdom and no reason to be scared.

So I see that in a way, YES, I am a New Mommy *pala*.

To my Teacher and Ate, I get it finally, thank you. Thank you so much.

Before I go I'll do something *Inception*-esque here. Back in 2013 when I was just starting out with the surfer dude, I got the chance to see Teacher in the principal's office, Quezon City.

I was full of *kilig* and first-time feelings, so when he asked me, "How are you, Mimi?" I couldn't help but dive into a story. As always.

After describing our rocky adventures, I remember ending with,

"…and I'm just not sure," I said. Teary-eyed but with a smile.

He did his Teacher thing like he always did. He said, "Go for it, Mims. If he makes you smile, if he makes you feel that way, GO FOR IT."

I stopped silent crying.

"Listen, Mims. Look at me. I'm XX years old and I haven't found the one yet." I laughed thru tears. I didn't MEAN for him to put himself down like that or be honest like that at my expense.

Yes, I remember there was so much love and hope in the room. We were both wearing blue and he was wearing a Marvel shirt (Captain America?).

"I've never felt that way before, but, Mims, YOU do. So that's IT. Go."

And I *did*.

That's why he will always be "Teacher" to me.

I got some of my old journals back.

It was emotional having my thoughts and feelings read aloud by my six-year-old.

There was the part where I said I wanted to be a journalist when I grew up.

She asked me, "Well, why didn't you, Mom?"

I teared up and said I wasn't strong enough back then. Not smart enough still, lol.

She said, "Well, I think you ARE. And you can write whatever you want NOW."

So here we are.

Everything was going great until we read about the airport and she misunderstood. She thought I would never come back. She thought me and my sibling got separated and we would never see each other again lol.

She cried because we had to say goodbye.

I cried too thinking about that.

So it made her think it was true. We were just going on and on and on and will someone stop the waterworks!

It took a while to calm her down. I had to tell her multiple times it was all OK, the reason we have these journals in the first place is because her Ninong retrieved them for us to read!

She laughed. We laughed.

And that was that. We then said goodnight.

The next morning she wrote on the last page. She wrote "Isla and Mia." She asked me if she HAD to keep a journal too like me.

I told her it would be nice if she did. Good writing exercise. If she had any feelings, just keep it and write it down. She made a decision and asked me if it was OK. I said of course it was OK if she does **what she wants**. She doesn't HAVE to.

I mean *I* did, and it's nice for me to have it now, it is, but she doesn't HAVE to have a journal. She can receive journals and diaries; they're gifts! Gifts are blessings and out of my jurisdiction.

But like me now, I am not OBLIGATED (as Ms. Rabina's voice rings out, "UTANG NG LOOB!" Rest in peace) to write about *mga anak ko*. I don't HAVE to keep a blog or post my child like I have a content calendar if I don't want to. I don't have to update about our whereabouts or post every second. Similarly I don't look differently at parents who DO have their children on social media. Because they are the parents. They decide. Right?

I can make my own rules for them and not do what other parents do. I can also try to do what other parents do if I see it's a nice way to go. **Nice!** I have these choices pala. Then if my two *bulilits* grow up and they want to do what they want to do when they're ready, well, by all means go for it!

I'm not writing to "get to a part" anyway, I'm writing for ME. And Isla and Mia can live for themselves too. As they wish. When they're ready.

But for now I'm not her best friend. Good. That makes it easier to enforce these rules and be JUST be her mom. Ha.

One of the reasons I like writing is I can never be wrong with my words and feelings. I can have WRONG THINKING, but if I am thinking it and not hurting anyone or taking a dig at anyone, then I'm just expressing myself. My hobby. I THINK I can never miss the shot or choose the wrong answer or explain the equation or you know. I don't have to THINK; I can just FEEL. Makes sense to me.

When I look back, I see my triumphs. Thing is what was grand in my eyes, well, in hindsight, was NOTHING at all. Just…ordinary. Random. Boring? Should I say?

Maybe.

But it was not boring to me at that time.

At that moment it was a story.

Children have stories. Old people have stories. People OUR age? Like me? We have reactions. I don't wanna listen to me. Things happen to me, and since I am learning still, I unfortunately let the emotions guide.

That's why I like the ends of the spectrum. Either I'm with the kids or I want to hear from older, wiser folks. I have to learn.

Norma is a seventy-six-year-old English professor who teaches language and essay writing at the nearby college. She's Filipino and lives on the floor above my mom. On occasion we are lucky to see her and hear her stories about school, her students, her life.

Norma is certainly a character. She has NO filter. In the '70s, she was married to a U.S. Air Force officer for 17 weeks until he was sent to Vietnam for the war. Coming back the plane got shot down and crashed with her husband on it.

"OMG! Did you have children with him?" I asked, wide-eyed.

"How the HELL do you think I would have time to get pregnant?!" she answered.

I swallowed and snickered.

"I just MET the guy! 'Course I didn't have kids with him. No!"

It was then I knew to never interrupt her again. I've seen her somewhere before, but as everyone IS one of a kind, let's just say she was a combo of Professor McGonagall, Miss Trunchbull, and Ms. Sibayan.

Norma said she later married a Norwegian and they lived in Norway for some time. They had two sons, one of which LIVED with her until he was FORTY. She recently bought him a condo so he can "get the hell away from me," lol, in her words. She LOVES him but cannot LIVE WITH him.

Norma is outspoken and intelligent, and you can tell that once upon a time, she was a looker. Refined. Class. Hard worker. She said that when she was young, her parents had no money to pay for her ballerina dreams, so when she was eighteen and COULD pay for it herself, she joined a beginner class. Of little ballerinas. A class for ages six–nine! She was the only eighteen-year-old in a TUTU! How great is that. How darn great.

Norma calls my kids her "*apos*." She says my second baby looks like me, but the first one doesn't.

I showed her a family picture, the four of us.

First thing she said? "Oh, you married a Filipino. I could never do that. I don't want that nose in my family."

I laughed and said,

"I married for his heart, not his looks."

She smiled.

Touché.

"Where is he now, *saan yung daddy nila*?" she asked.

I explained.

"Oh. That's good."

After reading some of my short stories and public journal entries, Norma told me I had "it." She told me, "Do not waste it." She pointed to me and told me not to stop.

"And by the way, your mother showed me pictures of you," she said as she was turning to go. "I said you're pretty in pictures. But prettier in person."

I said, "Thanks, Norma. Not that I need validation on my looks, but thank you!"

"KOREK KA JAN HIJA," she said. "You don't. You don't need to be validated on your looks OR your words. Keep going."

So I am.

Dear Kobe,
　　　It's me.

I idolized you growing up. You mean a lot to me today.

I had your poster on my wall. Only had three up there: Spider-Man, Britney, and you. I thought, I'm such a fan. But was I? Was I really? Or did I just join the bandwagon?

I loved Laker games because my dad would take a break from work and come home to watch. And whenever you'd win, he'd cheer, and I imagined I had something to do with his happiness.

I never even saw you play at Staples Center. I promised myself I would. That haunts me to this day. I was right there. RIGHT THERE.

Whenever they asked me in school, I always answered that you were my idol and inspiration.

But did I try for you?

No.

I'm sorry.

You were all over my notebook. Big Diesel, Fish, Fox, Horry, #8. Instead of my history books, I studied your pictures and calendar instead. Maybe that's why I had to repeat geometry.

I know it's so silly to even ask this, but would you still have advice for me? I never played. But would you still embrace me or let me hug your leg if we met and I asked?

Some nights I wonder. I'm so far from what you would think or consider to be successful like you, but if you were here, would you love me too? Would you be open to coaching me? Would you be proud to have me as a fan?

It's so farfetched, I know you're so busy and have so many fans already. I know. It would be hard to get in line and be seen by you.

I was devastated when I heard. I thought it was a joke. I couldn't breathe. Then I saw the same news over and over. And I thought, gosh, these people KNEW you? They got to converse with you, play with you, text you, and I…loved you from afar.

I should have tried more for you. I never ran up and down the court. I had the chance too. So, so many times. Why didn't I, why?

I was just so scared. Fearful of myself. I know you would have rolled your eyes.

I'm sorry that I never learned how to play, and now I don't have my own jersey to pass on to my girls.

All because I was in my head. Whenever I did step on the court growing up and the ball came whizzing to me, I was scared to catch. I wish you taught me how not to be. Not to be scared.

On nights I can't sleep, I watch your videos. Not your game highlights or documentaries. I just watch you speak. I watch you on late night. I watch you comment on your game. I watch you answer the easy questions and the hard questions too.

I watch your friends speak about you. I like hearing what Shaq or Matt Barnes or T-Mac have to say about you. They hated you on the court but admired you for the man off of it—a father, friend, mentor, and God-fearing champion. I love that you fought for your wife, I love that you loved Disney and went to Disneyland on your first date, I love that you were a girl dad.

I think about how much Gianna and you look so much alike—my firstborn and her father look so much alike too. Then can I be Vanessa? Ha!

I'm trying my hardest to be a better me and adapt the Mamba Mentality. It gets tough on some days. I flinch so easily. I give up so easily. I wouldn't make it with you if you coached me.

Even so. Would you be proud if I tried one shot? Just to show you I can shoot from the three-pointer

135

line. I'm rusty, but I wish you were here to watch. And see me try again and again and maybe, just maybe, I'd make one swish in front of you. That would be nothing for you, huh, but that would be everything for me.

If I missed though, would you rebound it still and pass it to me?

Recently I found myself at the top of the key. Free throw line. Only it wasn't a real court, it was just a kiddie one. For the kids. The dribbling brought me back, and I thought for a second I had it in me. Like in *Like Mike*. So I took the ball with the unicorn and rainbow print, probably two sizes smaller and lighter than the Spalding, and I released it.

Airrrrrball!

Hahahahha.

Tell me WHY I thought I would make it. I looked around and I thought, please, I hope no one saw this disgrace. A dad saw. OMG. I knew he was a dad, he was carrying kids' bags and jackets.

I was seen. SEEN. And he slowly shook his head, probably thinking what in the heck. I laughed.

I laughed.

It was too uncontrollable. We had to get out of there, quick.

See how much you help me now? I'm so far from where I want to be, but you pop up everywhere I go and tell me I'm going to be OK. So I think I'm gonna be OK. Because you say so. Thank you.

I can't sign as your number one fan or number anything.

It's just me.

Thanks, Kobe.

It's so loud.

Can't concentrate without breaking into a novel. I have to calm myself down before I'm arrested for going sixty an hour, and I mean my mouth.

Doesn't matter if the person is new in my life or someone has returned. Good. That's actually good! I'll use them as a portal to the past. What was that in Dumbledore's office where he had memories swirling about? The cabinet? The PENSIEVE! I got you. That, that's what I'm talking about.

I can be mid-sentence. But then it just APPEARS loud and clear and so vivid like what happens to Wednesday Addams or Phoebe from *Charmed.* OMG.

There I go again, imagining I am a character in a series or thinking I look like these people when, in fact, no, I'm just...me.

Darn me.

With these flashbacks I just remember the names I've been called.

"Just a GIRL."

"Just a MOM."

"Annoying."

"Inept."

"Selfish and ungrateful."

"Angel."

I remember.

The words. The conversations.

I try not to make my outbursts so public, no, that's just not right. I have to be aware of what's happening in the present. Can't miss a step.

But then I just HAVE to be in an enclosed space with a stranger. For fifteen minutes. That's it; we're DONE for.

"You have good vision, Camille. That's great. So whatever you've been doing, keep going. It's working," my optometrist said.

I couldn't place him in pop culture. I mean that's what I do, not to be offensive, I guess it's a calming tactic for me to be at ease with the person I'm talking to. If I can relate them to someone I've seen before, then it wouldn't be so hard for me to open up, to keep a conversation. But I couldn't with him, he was wearing a mask. As he should. Where was mine?

"Really? Doc, that's great! Thanks for saying that!" I exclaimed. And of course I did go on.

"Doc, this WHOLE time I thought my vision worsened. I mean I've been remote, so I don't SEE GREEN as much as I should. But! I've been eating better. Healthier. And the nursing is helping, excuse me." He shook his head to say it's OK. "But her medicine and her diet help me. They've helped my eyes! This is great news. All thanks to you. You're a good doctor, Doc."

"That's very nice of you to say, sweet of you, but no, the improvement in your eyes is all YOUR doing. You have been disciplining yourself, I see. It shows," he countered. "Me, I only CHECK the eyes. But keeping them healthy, that's all YOU."

Humble person. I like you already.

"Doc, I don't mean to pry," I started. My favorite.

"No, not at all. Go ahead. What's on your mind?" He was talking while writing notes on his notepad, how professional. How do they do that!

"Can I ask before studying eyes, before doing what you do now, what did you like? Like what were you interested in before ophthalmology?"

"Optometry?" he corrected me, lol, and answered, "Well, I've always had a love for science. Ever since I can remember."

DARN IT. I was trying to arrive at a point. I'm sure you know!

"Science and math. I enjoyed experiments. And then as I grew up, I realized I wanted to HELP people.

And I like talking to people. Like telling them about their eyes, giving them vision tests. Like what we just did!"

"Doc, the reason I asked was because I thought maybe in another life, you were doing something else," I said. "Like you were a life coach or something."

"Life coach! Ha!" He laughed. His eyes squinted and he relaxed on the rolling chair. "You know actually...I also considered taking up psychology—"

"That's it!!!" I said with a smile and, I'd imagine, a glimmer in my eye. "Psych. No wonder you're so good at this."

"Aw, why, thank you for saying that, Camille. Really sweet of you, but again your eye care is all thanks to you. Hats off to you there!" What a kind guy. Give this doc a hundred PTO days! He said, "And I saw the two outside. To be able to raise them? That's the hardest job in the world. You're doing great."

Please no crying, please no crying.

"Doc, do you have a family?"

"We're trying. I just got married over the summer."

"That's great! Congratulations to you!"

"Thank you, thank you. Yeah, we're trying and I want one or two, but I'll wait for her signal when she's ready."

"That's so wonderful, Doc," I said. "Well, I hope it happens for you. Whatever you want. When the time is right, I hope you will get that blessing."

"Thank you, Camille, so kind of you."

"No, Doc, the REAL kind one is YOUR WIFE! For choosing YOU!"

We laughed.

"Doc, sorry to double pry. Sorry I'm eating up your doctor time," I said in a hurry. I knew my munchkins couldn't wait any longer. "Where did you and your wife meet? Does she do eyes too?"

"Yes. We met in med school."

I LEAPT and I mean LEAPT out of my seat. "That's so beautiful! Congratulations again! You will make a great, great dad someday. Not just because you do what you do, I mean I'm sure you're very good, but because you're a life coach."

He said thank you for the hundredth time.

Gosh, my interview with him took longer than my appointment, lol.

"I have to go. I have to tell my husband I have good vision, thanks to you! Bye, Doc, thank you! See you next year!"

I love being alone.

I get to think about myself first. I never really did that before. I mean I did, but for some reason, I always put myself down first thing in the morning.

That's not a good habit. That's not how WE are going to live. That's not what my girls need to see and hear first thing in the morn.

I realize it now. I was chasing time and growth, but after all that chasing, I put myself LAST.

Stuck in Neverland.

I'm finding the pixie dust myself.

Hurts. In the past I realize either I put myself last or didn't put myself on the "to-do list" at all. Not fair to me. Not fair to my individual voice.

Not anymore.

Being alone and with a supportive team is good…I discovered it's OK. And I love that part. The discovery.

I love seeing the holes in me and realizing that I'm gonna be the one to save myself. Like I don't have to make the holes disappear, no; fortunately or unfortunately they're there. They happened. They are scars. Battle scars. They make me…me. I'm fine with them now. Before I thought they made me ugly and unworthy.

No, the scars make for good stories.

I wanted to prove that I liked music outside of the sugary sweet, pop kind of square I put myself into. I mean I loved it, my original soundtrack, I do, but since I was in a new place where they didn't know a thing about me, I wanted it to my advantage. Let's do offense this time, not defense. Let's start with something I DID know—music.

Now it was the Chris Brown, T-Pain, T.I., Ne-Yo era, and I loved their smooth sounds. I felt like I could DANCE when I really couldn't, haha.

CB, my name? It was before his relationship trouble, so HEY! I liked the guy. Besides I like him for his creativity and craft, NOT for the way he dresses, acts around women, or the way he presents himself. The guy's a father to three kids with three different women. That's not me. BUT if I like your music, I like your music. Doesn't mean I'm for his lifestyle.

Me and Anderson connected on music and Chris Brown. Anderson had his thing already. Could break dance. Could beatbox. I thought cool. Finally. Someone not afraid to show his talents. Could learn a thing or two from that.

CSA senior year section 4-I, Adviser Sir Robert Libao, elective journalism. I was singing to Chris Brown and Ne-Yo when a beat just dropped. Anderson just swooped right in with a beat. Just started beatboxing. I kept singing. Kept rapping. He kept beatboxing. We didn't even tell each other to go, I just kept rapping one verse after the other and he didn't question it, he just KNEW what beat to play next. I sounded so bad alone. OMG! Yes, I know I do, but with him acting as my minus one and second voice, all of a sudden, hey, I actually sound like the studio version, lol! I was the lead singer again!

When the song ended, we just looked at each other at the same time, same tone of surprise, same wide eyes, same incredulous reaction like: "What in the... we...what?! Cool! Camille, you didn't tell me you could RAP!" And I told him it's "'Cause you never ASKED!"

So we planned and collaborated for my five minutes of fame on stage. We practiced a bit for the senior fair. He had an act set up already, and he said he would call me up the stage to be his surprise guest star. I said, "OMG, no. No." I thought the last time I was on stage performing, I was...Oliver. And no one saw. No.

And now he was asking me to go on stage again, this time with the whole senior batch as audience? No. No.

But…OK!

Didn't take too long to convince this "Shawty." Hahahahaha.

Day of the performance, he did his thing. He called me up stage. On the mic. He said MY name. I felt people's confused stares and eyes. It was heavy. The oxygen flow to my brain stopped, causing me not to move a muscle.

I thought, do I go? Can I ignore it? Can we just CANCEL this actually! My crush was there. The girls I was trying to impress and be friends with were there. My classmates were there, and if I made a fool of my-self, they would turn their backs I'm sure. But WHY, ANDERSON, WHY, he just HAD to call me on the mic to join him!

He called my name again.

Come on, Camille. We rehearsed this. I couldn't leave him hanging! I did a Hail Mary.

I walked up the stage.

I did my thing.

What were my classmates thinking I thought, I THOUGHT that THEY thought this looks so bad. Last year she was a quiet new girl, and this year she's prob-ably gonna lose it.

Maybe that was right. I think I did.

Oh, I LOST it.

"Shawty, let me holla at you, you so hot, hot, hot, hot
You think I'd be hollerin', if you not, not, not, not?
I'm king of the town, you can take a look around
Teddy Penderaz down is in the spot, spot, spot, spot
Yeah, I got money on me
Yeah, baby girl, no problem
Yeah, you rollin', shawty?
Yeah, let's hit McDonald's
It's TP and CB, I'm a Nappy Boy
Oo-oo-ooo-WEEeeEeE!"

Sir Libao had a hat and shades and had moves pa, and the F-4 boys acted like his backup dancers. I don't think that was in the script, but that made it BETTER. To see my TEACHER jamming to me and Anderson. My gosh. What a highlight.

I scanned the crowd when I was done. No ONE reacted like I thought they would. On the contrary they all smiled. Not a single raised eyebrow. Not one. Maaaybe there was a "What Just Happened" look or two but nothing that made me feel low. Nothing that made me regret answering my name.

Thanks, 4-I and Anderson, for my one and only moment on stage. Most likely last of my singing career, lol. I can't battle against my girls, *alam mo naman.*

IF I am called out of retirement I guess. *I guess.*

Alone or with a crowd, the common denominator is me. I'm there. These stories. It's me. I make my own happiness and light.

And nowadays I like looking at my reflection and seeing someone who can make it to tomorrow if I survived yesterday.

What I'm doing is UNDOING and it feels good, I'm doing this for no one else but for myself.

And it feels like magic.

Ooooooh...now I know where this bout of girl power and confidence is coming from.

Tita Jessie.

LA after the wedding, we were invited to the Fernandez family get-together. I thought, how exciting! My favorite time! It's been forever!

It was lovely seeing them for the first time in a decade. We did see each other in passing when we came home in 2019, and we hugged and had short introductions, but those were under different circumstances. We didn't rejoice back then.

But there at the park, I was so full of love and memories and joy. I felt so free. Being there with my kin. Seeing my big kid run to her cousins she never met before and hug them tight like they've known each other her whole life.

We became kids again.

The set-up was marvelous of course. The picnic tables. The coolers. The *latag* on the floor. The sun was beaming, but I didn't feel it. We bathed under the sun, no umbrellas in sight.

One was comfortable in the shade, though, quiet. Henry, my cousin who blocked me numerous times when I was a kid. An enemy! Ha. He said hi to MY Henri. Gee. Why is this moment so NOW and so, so vivid to me. The paper plates. The *pancit*. The Porto's.

The grown-ups watching from the sidelines, making sure everything was in place. Quiet, observing, only speaking when spoken to, like guards on duty. There was Uncle Pete watching over the food, Uncle Loy watching over the kids. Then they would switch. Rotate.

I imagined the dads standing there too. I felt a rush of emotions. No tears this time. Just blank, pure happiness.

I was so in a trance I guess, I didn't realize that my first kid already helped herself to some pancit and chicken. And she found a spot already, right in the middle of the crew, right with Tita Jessie. My second kid? Somewhere, lol. But that's OK, I had a lot of extra hands.

Isn't that something? Tita Jessie has TWO DAUGHTERS. Each daughter has TWO DAUGHTERS of their own. So delightful.

At the wedding we attended Tita Jessie wore vintage couture. She came in her husband's Barong, shown below. Barong for Fernandez–Ivins nuptials in 1978. They celebrated their forty-fifth wedding anniversary last 2/18. Both their daughters wore a piece of her wedding dress on their big days.

Just lovely.

I said that out loud. Tita Jessie and I did a mom smile. I said,

"They're very lucky to have their Lola Jessie nearby. I'm sure you have so much to teach the kids."

"Oh, kind of you to say, Mimi."

She switched names, meaning guess we're FAMILY now!

"No, I don't do anything. They've GOT it. I just let them be."

We hugged. "You're a good lola, Lola!"

And she said, "And you're a good mom, Mimi. I can see it in Eesla."

I was gonna reply, but a sharp YELP echoed throughout the park. Ate Clarissa. OMG. I thought she threw Baby G in the air??? What was happening???

Everyone just screamed and one by one parted like the Red Sea, left and right. Out of the way!

A SNAKE crawled through our picnic! A snake!

Panic at the picnic! Make way for the ALAHAS!

Googled it, I mean AHAS.

Guess who grabbed the nearest giant stick and was ready to attack. "Let's go!!! Attaaaaaack!!!" she yelled.

NO!!!

The snake was put away after some time and we continued with fun on the carousel and more pancit.

I realized what I was missing. No, not the PLACE, not the FOOD, not the carousel ride.

I was missing self-love. Self-belief. Courage.

And Tita Jessie gave it back to me. She dug it up. Seventeen years since we last saw each other, and she gave it back to me just like that.

I told them that I missed them all.

All the picnics I missed came back to me tenfold. Thank you. Thank you.

God will bring us together again. In His time.

For now keep off the grass!

In a couple of days, we'll have to spring forward. I can't believe it.

Forward, forward. Move FORWARD, Camille! Growth and healing, remember? So why do I keep writing about the past? Why am I so into looking at these moments that are supposed to be DONE WITH?

They are all so poetic to me. I'm stunned, literally STUNNED at the music playing right now. Like quicksand my feet are stuck, and I am being pulled down and down and down and the only way out is to write!

See I'm just repeating myself. I need to stop this train or else I will run out of words. *Baka maubusan ako ng vocabulario*, lol.

I'm recycling words and ideas and I hate that. I don't want to repeat myself, because once it's done, it's supposed to be done. Right.

"Move on *na tayo jan*, Camille. Forget about Kobe. Forget about this and that."

But I can't move on. Not when the emotions are too much and these scenes are so ALIVE. I have to write about it and find myself in the process.

The feelings come back again during whatever time the DeLorean sends me back to. So am I doomed to repeat myself?

Doomed? *Or saved.*

Maybe there's a reason I'm being pulled back. I keep going back. Someone up there wants me to LEARN something.

Someone wants me to see NOW what I was too busy to see before.

The lights in my life, the small sparks of bravery and honesty…I see them now. It's too bright and I can't shut them away.

I showed Anderson what I wrote about him. On top of other nice things, he said that I remembered so much about high school, which was such a painful time for us all, haha.

Fourth year high school again. I'm sorry, I can't escape!

Orientation. Auditorium. We were SUPPOSED to be paying attention to the principal.

But of course we weren't.

Alphabetical order. The girls were together.

I kept to myself. Had to pay attention.

I heard whispering.

"Ikaw na!"

"No, ikaw!"

You, you do it, no, you! I heard them say. Naturally I became tense. I prepared myself.

"Hi! I'm Jane. Where are you from?" said the girl on my right.

The others giggled at Jane's straightforwardness. I'm guessing they were amused. Half-embarrassed, half-intrigued. They wanted to see where this conversation was gonna go.

As did I.

"I'm from California," I answered.

"*Ano sinabe*? What? Powerful?" she said.

Hahahahah. *Ang layo naman*, Jane. How did you get that?!

They erupted in laughter. I laughed too, but I was hesitant, nervous. Not because I didn't find it funny, I did, the situation was just too awkward and honest. I was just unsure about laughing (as openly as they were) because we were supposed to be QUIET in the auditorium!

They introduced themselves. I was at ease.

From then on we were known as the PowerFOOLS.

Oh wait, NOBODY referred to us as that. It was just us who called OURSELVES that name. Ha.

Nicole—tall, slender, model-like features; shoulder-length, thick wavy hair in a headband; full lips; big eyes. Eldest of THREE sisters. Her mom was a teacher at CSA. Nicole was always laughing. Always. Like she couldn't finish her sentences due to laughter and I loved it.

Jane brought the jokes. She started this whole thing. If she hadn't said hi, who knew. Who knew what would have become of me!

Jane had a nice voice and she sang in the school choir. I remember searching for her in line one day. She was supposed to be behind me. But they said, "Oh, Jane isn't in line with us today. She's in front." She wasn't in line with us BECAUSE she was up FRONT with the BAND! On the MIC! Gee.

I always sounded bad singing alone when we had worship songs, but Jane would just come in and do the second voice and like magic she made me sound ear-worthy.

Jane's bff was Miko. Good-looking guy, nice jawline, but—and no offense meant, Miko—at that time he was small and regular. You know what I mean. To me he looked like a young, YOUNG Filipino version of Orlando Bloom.

Hahaha, Camille, ang layo naman you might say! Well! OK fine, mix in Piolo Pascual's son. There.

That's Miko. That was the first time I felt admiration for someone who I didn't want to be together with. Like I thought he was attractive, I liked how he spoke straight Filipino, I liked his posture, but I did not want to HOLD HANDS with him you know?

Not MY person. Not Jane's person either. Still a very cool fella.

Miko and Jane never crossed the line with each other, but we sure had a party teasing them both. He was the calm, quiet one next to Jane's liveliness. Quiet. Always there next to her. Never really shared his opinion on things, just listened as we girls would chat on and on about what girls chatted about back then.

Anyway Miko always spoke in straight Tagalog. I liked that about him. When he saw me or when he joined a conversation, he didn't change his accent or dialect on my account, he just finished his thought or idea in Filipino.

I liked that. I did. I needed more of that. That realness and sureness. He didn't switch. Because I know I switched. I had trouble switching. But Miko...he was so sure. He didn't have to switch. Or pretend. Or be "*conyo*." He was just...himself. Like we'd be talking and then Jane would suddenly call him out and say like, "Oh, Miko, *ano sa tingin mo*?" And Miko would just say one thing or like a phrase that would make all of us erupt in laughter. And the great thing is, he didn't even try. It was just funny without him intending to be.

Miko. Don't know where he is now. Probably wouldn't answer any of my DMs if I tried reconnecting because he's a freakin' CELEBRITY in the Philippines now. I think Miko pitched to TV stations and read for thesis projects and *teleseryes*. He worked on himself, his body, his mind. His drive. He kept auditioning for short films. He took the small roles, the unknown roles. Found himself a seat in the makeup chair now. How cool is he.

I asked Jane what happened to Miko, she said, "Lol, I think *kinareer na niya talaga pagiging artista. D narin sya mareach*!" So Mike if you happen to read this very long love letter to 4-I, hi *naman*. KEEP GOING!

Rounding out the PowerFOOLs was Ana Choi. Quiet, petite, girly, giggly Ana. When she spoke about love, relationships, life, she was serious and true, and she had a sparkle in her eye.

I'm not sure what role I played, but I was certain that being with that group brought me to places. And by "places" I mean physical PLACES around school. I liked going around school with them, exploring the never-ending canteen, sitting by the stands, waiting by the bus. Nicole's mom was a teacher, so sometimes I walked with her to pick up her younger sisters and I'd see other parts of CSA. I saw other rooms and buildings that I just didn't know existed the year before.

With Nicole I felt confident walking to the faculty room to say hi to teachers. It was like I...stepped into a new place. But I was here already the year before that. What was this place? A Wonderland? I'll write myself in as "Alice" then.

With the PowerFOOLs' help and real friends in 4-I to back me up, I started to be OK in my own skin. I no longer rebonded my hair. I embraced my glasses. I started to raise my hand more. I felt OK going to other people's classes. I made jokes and told my stories.

I liked being in line. I liked the order. The familiarity. I liked seeing everyone in uniform.

Uniform.

And then I also liked seeing them in their "street," regular clothes too, because I saw them and they saw me, we saw each other.

It was the 4-I retreat. Time for reflection and prayer. Break from regular routine of school and homework to observe and pray. A lot of singing and being serious, which I really appreciated. We needed that. We needed to pause and be together. Girls stayed in one cottage, boys stayed in their own. Fun. Soirée.

Rules. No sneaking out. No drinking and other things. Mind the curfew.

But. It was Sir Libao in charge. Therefore there were no rules. Kidding! Let's just say that he let us get away with a lot.

I remember on the last morning of the retreat, I was the last to get ready. I went out to join the rest, but no one was in line or outside, so I thought, oh no, was I late? Did I not follow schedule? I looked everywhere.

They were upstairs. Gathered around, huddled around.

Without thinking I blurted out, "Guys? Is someone pregnant?"

Everyone slowly looked back. I remember Megan Shin, already *mataray yung* dating, even more mataray with her death glare.

Ana's eyes were red. Nicole's too.

"Oh, I'm so, so sorry," I said, inching closer. I didn't speak again.

Ana was with child.

She just found out. No one knew yet. The father knew—her husband now—but other than that, no one did. We didn't know what to do. What would we say to the guys? Sir Libao?

I remember Ana telling me she was scared to tell the boys in our class, who at that time were leader/captain of ACP (?) training the seniors had to do every Thursday (?) And she was scared to do physical activity already.

I remember that during breakfast, when we re-convened, I couldn't meet anyone's eye. But OMG! I spent the last few days connecting with everyone and kidding around and opening up and getting close, and all of a sudden…I didn't want to make the wrong move. We promised Ana we wouldn't say anything to the class until she said it herself.

Then she told them.

I don't know how it played out. I just knew that everything was going to be OK.

When we returned to the four walls of 4-I, it was as though we came back different…like…we weren't classmates…we were FAMILY.

We were protecting one another. No more groups, barkada, no more I just want to hang here, you stay there. You know?

It didn't take long for others to hear about the news from 4-I. Being a pregnant senior in a Catholic school was a big no-no. Every day I remember being scared for Ana.

Her skirt button popped. She was always hungry. She couldn't concentrate in class, she fell asleep. I think about it now and I'm like, gosh, Ana, you made it thru high school? All of that? So strong and amazing you are. I'm so proud to know you. Proud to know EVERYONE in 4-I.

Then Ana was told that she was unable to walk the stage for graduation. She was told she was getting her diploma but no stage moment. I felt so sad. So broken. The classmate I loved, the person who helped me feel included in a group, she was not getting this rite.

We had to accept it. We couldn't fight with the school. Rules are rules, no exception. We just had to keep our spirits up for the baby in the oven!

Being on a stage, well, that had its own meaning to me…and I'm sure it had so much meaning for her too. Ana was troubled at that time too, not sad she was having a child—no!!! Just upset that the friends she thought were her friends were in fact the first ones to criticize, judge, and spread the news. HER news.

I hated seeing her shaken world. She was GROWING a HUMAN and she had to deal with that? WHO said this, WHO said that? WHO made her cry when all she needed was love?

Well, it's GOOD and WELL I didn't know and don't know. Don't know who those people are, don't know who said anything.

Lol. As IF I would do something. Ya'll know that until now I can't pack a punch.

WHO said anything that made her cry? Nicole asked and Ana said names, but I didn't know who the heck. Literally WHO U. And Ana laughed. She laughed!

I was still connecting faces. *Mainam naman.*

We could have said forget about it, ignore it, yes, yes, but this is high school, people CARED what others thought, HELLO, that's what we did! Shoot, "I" CARED! We were kids, we didn't know better.

We know better NOW, but at that time, it was the end of the world!

We kept in touch after high school as we went our separate ways for college. The "powers" had to be evenly distributed.

Skip to working in PR, guess who's invited to all the mommy and lifestyle events? Guess who is being ASKED to attend launches or ASKED to write about brands?

Ana Choi.

That's right.

What a fun and inspiring bunch. CSA forever, and I'm glad we turned out to be PowerFOOLs. Still a fool, but I'm learning.

I wrote my dreams down on a notebook paper. In tenth grade as the clock was winding down to dismissal. I wrote it down. I wrote that I will get married at twenty-seven and have two kids. I wrote that we will live on Reseda next to my best friends.

I wrote down what our weekend activities would be—ha—Disney every month, every other Sunday would be lunch out at a Chinese restaurant or someone's house.

The minute I knew where I was going, I got rid of that paper. I thought it was a stupid, stupid paper. I never wanted to write anything like that again, never, ever again.

We all know life took us to different places. I'm not crying because I'm sad it didn't happen, I'm just crying happy tears because even if I didn't get what I wrote down, God didn't leave me and He brought me to what was MEANT for me.

He gave me the strength to fight for something else.

I got something instead, something that I can't even write into words. I have something that cannot be defined.

Maybe that's why on my wedding day, when it was time for thank yous, I couldn't even bring myself to talk properly.

I cried through my speech, OH PLEASE, WHY. I did. I guess all the emotion and stories and hope and the past and present and middle mushed up all together and it came out like that.

I'm not saying we will be OK, I'm not saying that we won't be either. At least I know that we will. *Will.*

That's it. Period.

WE. WILL.

Just those two words. Just. Those. Two.

"Everything happens for a reason. Eventually all things will fall into place. Until then we live for the moments, right?"

JC said that to me. I thought he was so *maporma* and popular when we first met. Again, no, it was nothing romantic. But there was this certain energy that drew me to him and his three other friends in communication arts. JC was in a relationship, so it was nothing like that. Honestly there was something about him…like he wasn't SUPPOSED to be here.

I felt like his smile wasn't really his…like he was there and happy, yes, but being there was so—excuse me, JC—like "*pilit.*" Forced. Was I seeing this correctly?

Like me comm arts wasn't my first choice. But I was there. It wasn't my first choice, but I was still happy I made that choice. Was he happy with his?

JC said that one day he hopes our families can meet, and I hope so too. I have to tell his wife this story, I HAVE to tell her LIVE and in person how I thought the world of these guys and I'm GLAD he did law after he graduated comm arts; otherwise he wouldn't have MET YOU. You see. Gosh.

Now I think, hey, I'm proud to know these fellas. They made college sweet. JC and friends were a band of brothers that saw me for me, and they did not turn around. They laughed WITH me, not at. But I ask myself, would they be proud of me? Would people be happy to know me? I mean, gee, Camille, you just live in your head nowadays, don't you? We're here living life and achieving dreams, and you, poor you, just writing in your journal?

Is it sad? Am I?

I had a good experience because of other people, but I'm afraid I was not so significant to anyone.

I wish I stood up for myself more.

I was scared. I am still, and a bit lost too, but making a bit of progress. Scared of the future, of being a mom, scared of me.

Favorite word of the English language?

Euphemism.

It has Philippines in the middle and ends with "M," which stands for me.

ME.

"Euphemism. Noun. A mild or indirect word or expression substituted for one considered to be too harsh or blunt when referring to something unpleasant or embarrassing."

Quick search says, "We use euphemisms to make things sound better or at least less offensive."

We've been using it since we were young:

"Seniors" or "Generation 1" instead of "Oldies."

Sounds great to me.

I also like words with silent letters: doubt, knack, foreign, write, aisle, my daughter's name.

I like that. The letter is silent, but without it the word wouldn't be...the word.

Silence is necessary for the word to exist, how beautiful.

The future is scary. So much is unknown. I can't tell what tomorrow brings, I can only know myself.

I can only try to know my girls.

If I know myself a little better, then that would be progress for me. Like why am I the way I am, why am I weak, what makes me laugh, what makes me tick, what makes me cringe, what makes me shudder, what makes me unsteady.

Since I am learning more about myself thru my weaknesses, then that fear and uncertainty will be bearable.

It won't go away, no, never. It's there for us for a reason. We will always have struggles. But once I find myself, then I'll be brave enough to face those struggles.

I will find a way.

A lot of this comes from pent-up anger.
Anger at the world.

Anger that there was a pandemic.

Anger that they took Kobe from this earth.

Anger that they took my love away from me.

Anger that they laid me off.

Anger that I had to cancel plans.

Anger that the two people I needed to hear from were not around.

Anger that I had to be a teacher to my then-toddler. I had to be a happy preschool role model, but inside I had so many questions, so much anxiety.

Anger and confusion. One by one people that were supposed to be brothers and sisters were turning against one another. I thought, what kind of example is this, for my baby? For me? I needed hope and light, but the world outside kept falling apart, kept proving me wrong.

As months passed in 2020, there was more anger.

More anger at the pressure. More anger that we had to stop every damn thing, but still life went on.

Anger that my voice was gone.

Anger that my choice was gone.

Anger that I forgot what sunshine felt like.

Anger that I forgot how the waves felt like—ha! Never mind I don't swim. I mean I missed how the ice-cold water kept my toes warm by the shore.

Anger that I was paralyzed.

Disarmed. Unheard, unseen.

Anger that through it all, I had to put on a brave front for my daughter. I had to be happy for her. I just had to keep going. I didn't know how. I didn't. But someone knew how. Someone did. My angels were there.

They made me realize, yes, I could stay angry. The emotion you are feeling is valid. Everyone was probably feeling this way, so I shouldn't think I was a pearl—HA! I wasn't one in a million.

You can be angry, Camille. But what? So what? That will destroy what's left of your light. Don't let it go out. Think of your daughter. Your future. Fight. Keep going.

Just being angry, no, that's not how He wants us to live.

So I asked Him, why? Why did He? Why did He do us like Noah's Ark? Why did He put me here?

Ha. So I'm angry at the same person that put me here. The same being who is going to save me.

Should I curse Him? I wanted to. Why not, right? But He GAVE me the words to SPEAK, so how DARE I use that same ability for curses.

No, no, cursing the one who gave ME LIFE is not right. Instead. Do something with that anger, Mim. Like Uncle Ben said, "With great power comes great responsibility."

The anger. Channel it somewhere.

So it started as notes to myself. Grocery lists. Lists of songs to listen to. Maybe songs Henri would like to hear when he came back, starting with BTS's "Boy With Luv."

Lists of reminders, things to stock up on. Soap, face masks, rice.

Then the notes just grew and grew until this happened.

Instead of deleting my stories, I kept them. Before I crumpled the papers and threw my notebooks in the trash. No. Not this time. This time I hit "publish" instead. To remind me that these were once my words and thoughts. To remind me that if I made it thru 2020, the end of the world, then everything else is…child's play.

And I love playing.

I can't stop now. I'm really done for. I see something on Facebook I agree with or I like, I write. Maybe I see something that's not my cup of tea or I'm reminded of a poor experience, I STILL write. Either way I win. Lose. Whatever you wanna call it.

I used to play piano well.

I *used* to. I lost it somewhere along the way.

I took lessons from Ms. Sarah—a tall, kind-looking teacher, with black glasses and shoulder-length brown hair. She had thin lips and was always in neutral clothing.

Her house was nice. Simple, homey, a lot of brown. I liked it. All of my lessons where in her home, eventually, a recital too.

I remember practicing the scales. I remember asking her what a clef note was, I remember mistaking the "S" at the beginning of a song for an ampersand. I remember learning about the sharp notes and the flat notes and I thought, well, these notes sound so "off" to me! Why would they even have these notes in a piano?

But the sharps and flats...without them the song wouldn't be complete.

The song wouldn't be complete. We need sharp notes and flat notes in our lives...don't we?

I remember gaining confidence because I knew the easy five-minute pieces; I memorized the nursery rhymes. I could read notes. I could look and just read. I guessed them at the beginning, ha, but a lot of the times, my palms would be so sweaty, they would leave marks on the keys. I'm sorry, Ms. Sarah, I am. They got sweaty on her piano, and I'm sorry to say, my palms got sweaty on other things too. The basketball. The computer.

To say I was embarrassed of myself is an understatement. I was, and *still am*, very aware of my sweaty palms. At that time it all just went downhill from there. In church during "Our Father Who Art in Heaven," we had to hold hands and sing, I was just so scared that the person I was holding hands with would recoil or shudder or take their hands away and look at me with disgust.

I remember coming home from church one Sunday. Yes, it was Sunday. I was wearing church clothes. Back then skirts and dresses were just for church. I never wore skirts or dresses to school (to hide my scars). When we came home, I was very sad. Very distraught.

I remember playing the piano in the living room. Our piano was next to the fireplace. I sat there with the piano book open, but I wasn't reading the notes, no, I was playing by memory.

It was the first time I cried silently.

My vision was blurred by my tears. Warm tears raced down my face and landed with a thud on the black and white keys.

I was still able to play the song because I knew it by heart. Then I stopped playing because the tears plus my sweaty palms made it slippery.

That was the last time I played a long piece on the piano.

I saw pianos again, and I was always reminded of my childhood and happily playing, but I never felt the urge to learn again or play because, well, I just ruined everything.

Years later my brother-in-law, Paul, would play. So beautifully. So easily. The family would just say "Play," lol, and he would. Any song. He was quiet, but when a tita told him to play something, he did as he was told.

Whenever I'd visit Henri's home, Paul would play for us automatically. Or sometimes I'd still be approaching, I'd still be outside, and we would hear classical music.

Later I'd ask him to play any song so the baby in my tummy could hear. He played. And he played again for Isla's baptism. He played again for his father's funeral. Waltz. Beautiful.

A musical genius. He went to the University of the Philippines for music and now is studying to pass the entrance exams to medical school.

I'm rooting for you, Paul. This is your graduation present from your big sis.

I was laid off for the second time from the same company I've been with since 2018. When they told me, I felt…OK. I knew I was going to be OK. Truthfully I wanted a break to be with my children, my family, but I did not know how to tell my company. I did not know how, so God helped me tell them. I was nervous, overwhelmed, scared. Of course I was scared—two kids, husband in and out, can barely keep a house from falling apart, I'm far away from my best friends, I only have a few meaningful connections.

I did not want to fix my resume, honestly, that first week. It's too much sitting behind the computer desk, trying to write good things about me, trying to iron out my accomplishments. I just needed a break from the keyboard.

The keyboard.

The piano sits in the same room as my work desk. Being laid off again traumatized me, and seeing the piano brought back those childhood memories with Ms. Sarah.

But then I realized. Well, am I now going to swear off music too? OMG, no! Am I going to give up? I don't think so. I made it through the FIRST round of layoffs, didn't I? *This time will be different.* This time, I will use the aces with me. During the first time, my soldier was gone. He was here now. And during the first time, I had one angel. *I now have two.*

Mama wasn't going down without a fight.

The next few days seemed like one big hallucination.

I looked on the bright side: I could rest, relax, read a book, find out what I really wanted to do. I could do the things I was putting off for so long.

Then my husband lets me know he has news.

Oh…my…gosh.

I am the one who has news in this relationship. For HIM to say that HE does? Something's going down. Mayday, Mayday.

Henri just got promoted. "To what???" I asked.

Sargent.

He was aiming for a level up in his fifth year, but someone from above decided to break protocol, it seems.

Hold. The. Duck. Up.

Are there cameras in here? Am I being taped? Are we wired? Is Ashton about to pop out and tell me I'm being *Punk'd*?!

You're telling me, here we go, my husband just has to just PUNCH something and he freakin' gets to level up? And I...*what am I doing*?

See this is an ego thing now. Ego, lol, this is a game now, huh? Well, TWO can play that game.

Let me PUNCH the keyboard instead.

I went into a craze.

Red pill, blue pill. Two choices, right. Stay idle, mope, and cry in a corner or DO SOMETHING.

Which one, Camille?

BOTH. Ha! So I sent my essays to a few outlets.

Ding ding ding! We've arrived at your destination.

Someone got back to me.

This is an argument.

In an argument we are using words. Unfortunately for you your wife LOVES words and therefore if you take one more step, you're stepping on lava.

Barefoot.

If in this argument you use anything else BESIDES words, I will use my voice to call for help. And help will come to listen to WORDS.

They will decide who needs to be taken away from the children.

So let me summarize and cut to the chase before we go on.

You can think about arguing, you can think about talking back, you can think about rolling your eyes. But if I feel that I am not at EASE with you, my soldier, then please retreat to the barracks. Stay there. Set up camp.

Read.

Let's cool off.

And when you're ready to say you're sorry, I'll be right here.

I AM your New Mommy.

God can hear me.

Two years ago Isla and her dad went to Brooklyn to enjoy a "Daddy and Me" day (yay, no mom)!

Leaving the carousel nearby, a little blonde girl said to her dad, "Hey, that's Isla!" to which her dad kindly tried correcting, "You mean you THINK that's Isla? That girl LOOKS like Isla?"

The girl adamantly answered, "No, Dad, that IS Isla, from class!!!"

Coincidentally both pairs of daughters and dads went to their respective cars at the same time, which were parked, coincidentally, next to each other.

"Excuse me," said Marc, the other dad, who cautiously approached Henri. "Is your daughter's name by chance Isla?"

Henri was confused. How the heck did this random stranger know his kid's name? Still he took a chance and slowly said, "Yes…"

In that instant it was an explosion of unicorns and rainbows and foxes and glitter. I'm guessing that the dads did not have to say anything further, their daughters knew how to go from there.

God sends you angels. Thinking about this all makes me cry of pure happiness because of His goodness and grace. I was praying, praying for a simple sign, a moment, anything to help me ease my heart about in-person learning and school, and it came in the form of Nora and her family.

Oh, anak, sometimes there's coincidence, and sometimes there's fate, and sometimes there's making things work by communicating and compromising. Whatever it is it's all God's doing and His love that will pull us through. I thought to share this story because it lights up my day when I think about it. Nice reminder that sometimes great things can happen when Mom's not around.

I have a dark side. I have a mouth. You know I get emotional. The person reading this knows. But I am trying to break away from bad habits and poor cycles. I am trying to stop thinking negatively of myself even before the task has begun. I have to stop putting myself down. That is unfair.

I have to love myself because no one else will. I'm not talking about romantic love or familial love, but you know self-love. **I need to bet on me**. I need to.

I will set boundaries for myself and for my family. I will not give in to that dark side! I will fight it! I will heal my own self; God will show me how. I will grow from it. I will be my own cheering squad. I will sing my song. And if you sing with me, great, better for me so I'll be in tune. And if you don't sing along, you don't have to, I respect you and I'll be fine by myself. If I'm alone, well, then even better, I get to be a host just like my *kumare*!

This year has been so much of me fighting with myself, fighting with my past. This year has been so many questions. Life will be so many questions. It will be. But because I have you both, anak, and your dada, I will always have the answer:

LOVE. Love is the answer.

"Love will save the day."

That is one of the songs in the movie that was on repeat for the most of 2021-2022. Camila Cabello's version of Cinderella on Amazon Prime saved me. The music, the dancing, the modern songs, and the familiar characters. It was Isla's favorite movie that year. Her favorite song was "Million to One," written by Cuban–American singer Camila. Camila. So CLOSE to my name. Camila used to be in a group of five, but she broke away and became an independent, top-selling artist. To me, she's the best singer. To me, she is the prettiest one. To me, she is the most successful. She is petite and she is of Latin roots, so she is diverse.

I AM NOT any of those things, except diverse lol.

I am not any of those great things that she is.

But Camila taught me to be brave, to be strong, to just do what you love. For her, it's singing and dancing like no one's business. For me, it's writing.

So maybe I am not her, but *I AM ME*.

And that is enough.

One of my favorite past times is going at it with Isla. Like arguing with her. Debating with her innocent determination. Fighting over nothing. We're not even fighting, we're just two forces colliding and the thing is, no one can UN-COLLIDE us.

It's up to us.

I hate using the "Because I'm your MOM" card. Not fair. No, you shouldn't follow because I'm your mom. Because I admit that as a mom, I have made mistakes.

WE follow because it's what's RIGHT. When there's a day I'm no longer on this earth, you don't do it because it's what "I" would have done, what you think I would have wanted. I mean, yes, you can, but you don't owe me anything, anak, thank you though. You do it because it's what YOU CHOOSE to do. And you're choosing to do what's right. We choose Him.

Hey, if I'm wrong I'm wrong. If I'm not doing this right, well, that's our fate. At least I'm trying. And I'm trying it my way. I see the mom blogs. I see the movies. The books—the summaries, at least. I have the best guides in my life. But the one doing the dance *has to be me*. Fortunately or unfortunately it's me, mga anak.

Someone once told me to have some self-respect. Up until my late, late twenties, I did not know what that meant.

Self-respect.

I know what both words mean individually, but together with a hyphen?

No.

I'm sorry that I didn't know it sooner.

I mean before when I heard it, I would really think that the word is just something you spell in the spelling bee.

Self. Self. As in like self…ish? All about me? So myself? All about me?

Respect. I know what THAT word means at least! Ha.

Respect your elders. Respect Mother Earth. Respect the flag. Respect the church. I have an idea. We can sing about it too, Aretha Franklin belts out, R-E-S-P-E-C-T.

But the two words put together?

I'm not too sure, and I sadly admittedly was not aware until two years ago.

But in my healing, in my questions to myself and to God, I came to finally understand the meaning. Finally. After all this time.

My children will NOT have to wait until their late twenties to learn the meaning of self-respect. My children will know how to respect themselves. They will know what is right from wrong, yes, and they will know they have their own voice.

I am so, so sorry, mga anak ko, I didn't know it before. I am sorry to you for that. You will both need it. I think we will need it as we grow up in a man's world.

There are so many things I can't define, and I am so embarrassed that I have to look them up still, but one thing is for sure, I won't ever have to think twice anymore about this definition.

Isla and Mia, BOTH of you helped me figure it out.

It's a regret of mine not knowing my father-in-law longer. In one of our last moments together before his passing, Henri and I made *paalam.*

My mother-in-law started it off, and she said, "Dad*, may sasabihin sila sa 'yo.*"

Lolo Henry turned his attention to us. We had the floor to speak.

Goosebumps.

I don't even remember what Henri said. All I know is that he was the one who broke the silence. I sure could not speak at all—and THAT's saying something!

Henri stated our terms. It felt like we were holding each other. I know we were far apart.

"Good. Go," was what Lolo Henry said.

He didn't ask when, didn't ask why, didn't tell us to stay. He just smiled and nodded like he already knew the answers to all of the above. We didn't have to explain.

I guess he saw my worried face and felt my anxious mind/heart because he turned his attention to me and said, "Why, what's wrong? Scared?"

The thorn in my throat grew a foot longer.

I nodded. He said,

"What do you have to be scared for? You have each other. So work together."

He said it so simply. So matter-of-factly. Like this wasn't life changing at all. Henri and I exchanged unsure glances.

He continued,

"God is with you. You can do anything if you work together. Try together." And he added with a smile, "And if it doesn't work out, it's OK, you have a home here. You have us."

Cue the tears. I couldn't look at my partner.

"You can come home any time you want. Any time. But why would you? You have each other. Believe in each other."

Those words will echo tonight, and they will be with us tomorrow, next week, next month, next year, and until the day we see Lolo Henry again.

I sit here sometimes and think to myself, what would he say about me now? What would he say about us? Would he be happy we chose each other? Would he be ashamed? Would he be proud I'm still standing but NOT doing anything, just telling stories?

Would he hug me? I don't even think I got a chance to do that. Why, Camille? You had all this time? You didn't even hug your own father-in-law? One half of the unit who raised the love of your life? The person who LET me take his last name?

I fall asleep and sometimes curse myself because I am nothing. I curse his son for being everything to his family, for literally being the "hero" to his daughters.

I ask Lolo Henry, why did he want me for his son? What did he see?

Why did he have to leave us when BOTH of us had so many questions still? We have so many questions now.

Why is he not here now?

He didn't give me any of the answers. No. He didn't. He didn't give me answers at all.

But that afternoon in front of his wife and his firstborn son, he gave me something better.

He taught me how to fight.

Our love runs deep. It cannot be contained or explained. It just is, and that's what makes it beautiful. Like the ocean sometimes it roars, it crashes, it swallows anybody or any body in its path. Sometimes it's calm, so still, bone-crushing cold even. But if you listen closely, you can hear the waves play music.

People see what is on the surface, and they can formulate any idea or opinion they want to based on what they see, but the ocean doesn't change—it just... continues being...the ocean. Times will get dark, but the ocean can't run from the darkness. The night still comes. It just must be strong. And unwavering. And peaceful.

And the ocean must know that the sun will rise. And when the sun does rise, it will later come down again. Then come up, then go down. Then up and down. Up and down. Repeatedly. Over and over again.

But the ocean? Still the ocean. Still...*still.*

It cannot be contained or explained.

I don't have any medals. And you know why?

I'm not done learning. I'm not done with my course. I'm not done making mistakes. I'm not done growing up through the pain. I'm not done having conversations with my past. I'm not done with this level. I'm not done making a mess. I'm not done figuring it out. I'm not done! I'm still a work in progress. You wanna talk back? Be my guest. You wanna make jokes? The floor is yours. You wanna rain on my parade? Go ahead. *But I'm not done, and it's a dangerous thing.* I have yet to meet the best version of myself, but I know she's out there. If it takes months or years, I'm gonna meet her and she'll say, "I knew you could do it."

Falling in love is so fun. It's easy. It's smooth. You're falling and flying, and your head's in the clouds. But what happens when you fall down? Like you actually fall and something stops you from going any further?

What happens when you find that both of you are at rock bottom, when you're down at the bottom of the well and its miles and miles before you get up there? You see the light and you both want the fresh air.

Do you tear each other's guts out, a fight to the finish?

But what happens if both of you turn out to be fighters? One has the muscle and one has the spirit. You guys must work together and try your hardest to climb out alive. One has the senses and one has the...stories.

You're forced to look inward and ask, "Am I strong enough to get out of this tunnel myself?" Right now me, no. I'm still training. I hope, I wish, I dream, maybe so pathetically, that my words can get us out of this tunnel alive. I realize that it can't be me alone to get us out. It can't be your partner alone, either. It has to be you both.

I am a combination of the things I thought I failed at.

When I was a child, I thought I failed at basketball.

When I was a teenager, I thought I failed at writing.

When I was a young adult, I thought I failed at life because I did not graduate on time.

When I became a mother, I thought I would fail my daughter.

When I started a new chapter, I thought I would fail at every page.

When I was alone, I thought I would fail at being alone, because I never figured out *how* to be alone; instead I was too busy thinking I would fail.

I failed *because I did not try*. I let the voices rule my head and as a result, I did not follow my heart. I am ashamed and beaten because of that.

Not anymore.

After this book I will no longer second-guess. If I'm read by many, great. If I'm read by none, then I will pick myself up and try again.

Kobe said, "I'll sleep when I'm dead."

Kob, how morbid of you.

But now I understand. I do!

The passion. The drive. The need to grip the ball in your hands even when you're in bed. The willingness to beat you of yesterday.

Writing is like that to me, Kobe. I wish you were alive to tell me not to be scared. To hug me and tell me, even if my fingers slip, I'll be OK, I'll still leave a mark, right?

Whatever happens. I believe in myself, I believe in my words, and I will keep trying.

Most people who asked (or maybe did not ask, I just offered this story, lol) know why I (I mean *we)* chose Isla for our daughter's first name.

With the "S" silent, Isla sounds like "I love you." Henri has always liked the island life. Our funny adventures started in the Philippine islands. While I was pregnant and we were in early stages of partnership and disagreeing about bedsheets and dinner menus, I imagined that we would probably ALWAYS be disagreeing on something. Anything. It would get worse with time, right? But I knew no matter **how** heated the argument would get, no matter **how right or how wrong** me or Henri could be, bottom line is I love you. "I love you." *I love you.* That's why it's "Isla."

Second name is "Michelle." A more traditional name, and, yes, after Michelle Obama, First Lady of the United States (2009–2017). You know what they say! Behind every powerful man *is an even* MORE powerful woman. "CH" is there for Camille + Henri, and we keep the "-LLE" from my name.

Here we go again! Naming my second daughter— what fun! Let's see. Was I going to be as thoughtful and careful this time around? Mia. No, lol. Simple. Classic. Shorter than the already short Isla. But BE-CAUSE it was so simple and so ordinary and so plain and because it reminded me of the song "Mamma Mia," we went with it.

Runner-up was the name "Chelsea." I always did like the name Chelsea since I was young, ever since I played with Barbie and friends.

"CH" is together like in Isla Mi**ch**elle, and then there's "sea" at the end, which reminds me of the *Isla*-nd life my husband loves. Also ends in "a" like Isla does, but the vowel is not pronounced. So the names are *spelled* alike, but they are *not* the same. That's what I initially wanted.

Well. Overruled by guess who! And it worked out.

As you can tell, names have big meaning for me. I'm happy with what we chose. No regrets. I'm so glad I have a Chelsea in my life. Oh, I like her for the person she IS, but her name is def a bonus!

I told her that I was on a journey of self-discovery and healing, and I needed to see her family at the beginning of 2023. It was of utmost importance that the first interactions I had to start the year were meaningful. It was going to be *intentional* and be with those who brought me light and joy. For my peace and good vibrations for the next twelve months.

Chelsea so kindly obliged to my wish, and, to my excitement, we had a day. At the park. For me. The kids hung around the monkey bars and went up and down the slide but it was "I" who was having the real fun.

Oh! It was the talk of the town that their family adopted a dog, and Isla came home one day so happy, announcing that her best friend now owned a dog. I remember forewarning Chelsea that I was *not* a dog person, and Marc so kindly stayed back behind the gate with Louie on a leash just so I could be comfortable.

How nice is that? Why, why would they be that thoughtful? *I* had the dog issue, *I* should have been behind the gate ("With a leash!" Henri would add). We were in a public park. Dogs could run free. So *who* AM I to ask for Louie to heel when I was the one who needed to lay down? I am so sorry for my diva attitude, but you guys, why must you let me have that? WHO AM I to ask if their FAMILY DOG could stay away on their FAMILY DAY?! Please someone knock on my head.

So I said my thank you and apologized to both, and no one took my apology, lol, which made me more emotional.

We arrived at the subject of healing. Growth. Transformation. Good energy. Realness. True strength. I mentioned that I was not as strong as my partner, but oh, **I** so wanted to be. So bad. I told Chelsea I was doing one push up a day. She said GREAT. That it was a good start.

"I think you need to punch something," Marc remarked so nonchalantly, keeping Louie from *looking* at me. Lol, so sorry.

"You're darn **right I need to punch something, and he's waiting in the car right now**!!!" I fired back, and the couple laughed. We laughed.

I said, "You guys are amazing, so amazing. How do you do this? Three kids, a beautiful home near their school, independent, working, family oriented, no beat missing, and now *you have a dog*?! How do you NOT *lose it* on each other?"

Chelsea was pulled away by a wandering toddler, so she was unable to answer. Instead it was Marc who replied.

"Oh, we do lose it on each other. **She does** sometimes," he gave me a little smile. A little hint of a sparkle in his eye, like Dumbledore.

Chelsea returned. She missed the small exchange, but I had a feeling she knew exactly what her better half said about her.

"Here's what I think," she started. "We heal from our past. We heal from our past upbringing. Just because we heal or we break that cycle, it does not mean we are any less thankful or any less loving."

I yelled a "THANK YOU!"

She continued, "And this is something we've dealt with, Marc and I," she looked lovingly and so confidently at her husband, like it was a fresh lesson that they just learned yesterday, "Maybe the reason why the older generation is so hard on us is because they haven't healed from *their* own past, which in turn makes them project their own insecurities on us."

I stopped her. She was throwing too many big words at me. I told her I understood, but the conversation was getting too deep for a park day.

We laughed.

Then we went back to the swings.

Lunch was at this "make-your-own" pizza place near where I used to work. I was happy to be there, truthfully, because I had my first lunch break there when I started working in recruitment in 2018. It wasn't my first time.

But it was Isla's first time. And Anne's. And Mia's.

There was a life-size game of Connect Four on the table that was calling our name. We found a spot. No one else was in the restaurant but the four of us. There was no one else behind the counter but Ricky.

Ricky. Poor, quiet, lucky Ricky. Lucky that he got to wait on this chaotic quartet on their girls' day. He was tall and had facial hair and both ears pierced, I think his nose too. The diamond on his nose was blinding as the light bounced off the glass, protecting the pizza toppings. AirPods on either ear. Snapback. Resting face.

I told Ricky it was our first time ordering, it was our first time making our own pizzas, so we had a lot of questions. He shrugged and said it was OK if we did, that's why he was there, to help us make our own pizza. He said we can put whatever we wanted in our pizza. Whatever we wanted.

Anne went first. Thin crust. No tomato sauce. Olive oil. Ricotta cheese. All the greens. Spinach. Olives. Lots of arugula and mushroom.

"Is this OK?" she asked me.

"Is this OK?" I asked Ricky.

"Yeah, I mean, if that's what you want, then yeah."

Mama next. Thin crust. Tomato sauce. Olive oil. Mozzarella. Onions. Mushrooms. Sausage. Ham.

Isla last. Thin crust. Tomato sauce. Pepperoni.

"No cheese?" I asked.

"No."

"Is it OK, no cheese?" I asked Ricky. He shrugged and smiled.

"Is it OK that my daughter asked for no cheese on her pizza?" I repeated it slowly, like he was my therapist. Close but not quite.

"I mean," he looked down at us, looked from side to side, stifling a laugh—I HOPED he was going to laugh! "If that's what she wants, then YEAH, she can have a pizza with no cheese!"

We laughed.

"OK, no cheese then. We trust you," I said. Mia was fussy, her mama was talking too much. Still I went on as usual. "You would frown upon this if it wasn't going to be good, right? You're the pizza professional?" I said. "You'd let us know, right, if this was wrong?"

Ricky laughed. Guess he couldn't hold it in. "Yeah, but there's nothing wrong with that. I mean **make your own pizza**. This *is* what I am here for. You *can* make your own pizza. Do what you want."

I whispered to my sister-in-law, but Ricky could obviously hear. I saw him smiling out of the corner of my eye. "OK, he's not shaking his head or calling his manager, so we're in the clear."

I felt his quizzical gaze.

"We're not from here. Well, *I* am, but this is a new restaurant for my daughter!"

"Oh nice, where are you from?" Ricky asked.

My favorite.

"WE are from the Philippines," I answered.

"Nice! My best friend in elementary was Filipino," he said.

I asked how long the pizzas would take. Ricky said ten minutes. That was all? I told them to go back to their seats to play. "Dismissed!" and the three of them went back to our table, while I stayed behind to get our drinks.

Now I can tell when a person does not want to chit-chat. I can tell when a person is not interested in hearing more. The body language, the lack of eye contact. I get it. I do. I kept it casual. But Ricky opened up the conversation, OK, not ME!

He said, "So are those three your daughters?"

I laughed. "What? No, the two shorter ones are mine, the taller one is my sister-in-law."

We made small talk about the Philippines and like all my "small" talks, I eventually let Ricky know I was working on my first book. In the middle of telling him what it was about, Anne came and said the girls accidentally spilled the chocolate milk all over the floor. The pizzas weren't here yet, *meron na nangyari*, lol.

Ricky was so kind to give Isla a chocolate milk on the house.

I told Ricky I wanted him to be a part of my book.

"Sure, you can use my name, I don't mind," he said with a shrug.

"What? Really, Ricky, really. I am writing a book, and I am going to use *your real* name."

"OK. Go."

"No, no, no, no, no, no, Ricky," I said, so shocked. "I am writing a book, I don't even know if it's going to go anywhere, this could very well be a figment of my imagination. I have never done this before, so honestly this book could sink or float. Let's say it sinks. And if sinks so, so bad, like it stays at the bottom of the ocean, that's it. Your name will be in it. So I am asking you, *can I use your real name?*"

Ricky smiled. He reminded me of a past bully who once smiled at me, but back then it was a menacing smile. No, this one…it was different. Ricky was a friend.

"So? So what? I don't think it will sink. But so?"

"What do you mean 'so?' Ricky, this could ruin your name!" I said dramatically with a laugh.

"I don't think it will." He shrugged.

"Ricky, that's EXACTLY why you should be the *last* page in my book!"

"How old are you?" Ricky suddenly said.

I was taken aback. The last time someone asked me that was when I went to Taft High.

"I'll be thirty-three this year." I reacted to my own age. "You?"

"Twenty-six," he answered.

I told him that the last time someone asked me for my age, I was sad. I told him back then, people who didn't look like me were intimidating, and some were mean.

Ricky said why **wouldn't** they be nice to me. There's no reason *not to be nice*. "Why would they be

mean?" he said softly. "No reason to be mean. Like…
why?" I felt like he was really asking why, lol.

I called him so very nice. And smart. And one of
the best pizza makers I knew.

"Can I have your number?" Ricky suddenly asked.

I was shocked again. The last person who asked
for my number so straightforwardly like that, well, I
ended up marrying.

"What?"

"Can I have your number?" Ricky repeated. "I
need to save your number so we can keep in touch."
Tears were in my eyes. "So you can tell me when your
book is out. I'll go across the street and I will buy your
book."

So much joy.

"Text me, and let me know when I can buy your
book."

M ga anak, if you ever find yourselves at crossroads later in life, and if, for whatever reason, me and your dada are not around or unavailable, my wish is for you to go on a treasure hunt.

Find my teammates who passed me the ball. Find them and tell them your story. Time changes things, and situations may be different, but if you want to go on an adventure and I'm not there, Isla and Mia, just find them.

Find the people in this book. You will be safe and you will be loved.

Or you know what? If you don't want to find them, if you want to do your own thing, that's fine as well. Do your own thing. DON'T follow my wish. Make your own wish, believe in it, stand up for yourself, and follow your heart—whatever you decide. And we will love you, always and forever. You can do anything you can put your mind to! Look at this, for example: if your clumsy, silly, sing-songy mama can write a book about her random musings and share her point of view on simple things, then YOU CAN DO IT TOO. YOU. GOT. THIS!

Love always,
Mom.